Northern NURSES

True Nursing Adventures from Canada's North

Edited by J. Karen Scott with Joan E. Kieser

Canadian Cataloguing in Publication Data

Scott, J. Karen; Kieser, Joan E.
Northern nurses: true nursing adventures from Canada's North

ISBN 0-9730392-0-5

1. Nursing   2. Northern Nursing   3. Women's Studies   4. Nurse Practitioner
5. Northwest Territories   6. Nunavut   7. Outpost Nursing   8. Extended Practice
9. Environmental Health   10. Community Health Representative   11. Autobiography, Nursing

Kokum Publications
199 Queen Mary Drive, Suite 1505
Oakville, Ontario
L6K 3K7

jkscottrn@sympatico.ca

Photo design graphics by Laurie Quinn

Proceeds from the sale of this book will be donated to a northern nursing scholarship fund.

Printed and bound in Canada 2002
by Mothersill Printing (1988) Inc.
Second edition August 2002
Third edition May 2003

This book is dedicated

*to all those who provide or support health care
in the Canadian North*

*to all the residents of the North, who contribute to the
richness of the northern nurse's experience*

to the memory of Rick Tremblay

ACKNOWLEDGEMENTS

This book began when my call for northern nursing stories was printed in the newsletters of the Registered Nurses Associations of the Yukon and Northwest Territories (which now includes Nunavut), Alberta, Saskatchewan, Manitoba, Ontario, New Brunswick, Nova Scotia, Newfoundland and Prince Edward Island. The Aboriginal Nurses Association publication carried the notice, as did the RCMP Quarterly, and so my thanks go out to their editors. The University of Windsor Alumnae Magazine editor put me in contact with other alumnae organizations and carried the notice in his publication. The Nurse Practitioners Association of Ontario also placed the information on their website.

* * *

I would like to express my thanks to many individuals. Mary (Flowers) Wesko and Barb Round used their extensive network to put me in touch with northern nurses. Robin Kraft was a constant source of support throughout this project. Dawn Livingstone assisted by reading early drafts and encouraged me to proceed with the project. Dawn was very helpful with place names of the North, both new and old (see Appendix). Judy Comerford keyed in the handwritten contributions. I am grateful to Sue Pauhl for her assistance, and to Barb Bromley and Jan Stirling who encouraged me from the outset. I thank the Archives Division of the Prince of Wales Northern Heritage Centre in Yellowknife who kindly provided the cover photograph.

Liam Kieser was an angel in all things technical and I thank him for his support and guidance. He got me through two worms and a virus with my hard drive intact (and my feet on the floor) as the book progressed to completion. It was well worth the trips that Joan Kieser and I made to Stratford for the constructive advice of Gay Allison. Gay, our editorial consultant, was an enormous help in our efforts to fine-tune these wonderful stories. A special thanks to Lennox Grafton, our map and place name expert, who was a running source of insightful comments.

Finally, I am indebted to my long-time friend, Joan Kieser. Joan completed her Bachelor's degree at the University of Toronto and taught high school English for a number of years. Through the many hours of editing this book with me, she has shaped us into "Writers of the North." Thank you Joan for making this a special book.

INTRODUCTION

My first excursion into the North came in 1970 while doing fieldwork for Dr. Brian Lowry of the Division of Medical Genetics at the University of British Columbia. During that year, I visited almost every reserve in B.C. My most memorable trip was with a Health and Welfare nurse who took me along to Telegraph Creek. I had flown into Hazelton from Vancouver where she met me at the airport. She took one look at my jeans and cowboy boots and said, "I am *not* taking you dressed like that!" There was a scramble to find some thermal underwear and get me outfitted so I wouldn't freeze. As it was, I almost did. But that is another story.

Some years later, after I had finished a summer working at the Cystic Fibrosis Camp on Lake Couchiching in Ontario, I was sitting in a Tim Hortons in Orillia, wondering what to do with myself for the next year. I noticed a Health and Welfare sign across the street and remembered being impressed with their nurses that I had met in my travels. I pondered briefly, and always ready for a challenge, took a deep breath, walked over, and inquired about a job. A few days later, I had a call from Miss Skov in Ottawa, asking me to meet her at the Royal York Hotel in Toronto for tea. Thus began my twenty-five years with the Government of Canada.

Shortly after the Royal York interview, I was off to Sioux Lookout Zone where I wandered about the hospital for a few days, waiting for a zone nursing officer or director of nursing to appear. (I discovered later that I had been nicknamed Texas Lil because of my cowboy boots and my six-foot stature.) For the next two years, I worked in the Sioux Zone in New Osnabourg and Big Trout Lake and then as the Federal Public Health Nurse in Sioux Lookout. It was while on this last assignment that I was seconded to Povungnituk, PQ for a month. That story comes later in this book.

From Sioux, I transferred to a public health position at Six Nations near Brantford, Ontario, where I enjoyed working with Rebecca Jamieson, an educational consultant. After I had been there for two years, a poster crossed my desk advertising for ships' nurses. I applied, and two weeks later, I joined the Canadian Scientific Ship Hudson as Chief Medical Officer. Every summer we sailed into the high Arctic and in 1981, we circumnavigated North America. In 1982, ours was the first ship to reach the site of the Ocean Ranger disaster, where the crew recovered bodies under alarmingly dangerous conditions.

After four years aboard the Hudson, I moved back to Toronto to get reacquainted with the real world. My apartment just didn't have the amenities of the Officers' Mess, and not being used to cooking for myself, I was hungry for the first while. I was assigned to what was then called Revenue Canada where I did "boot camp" training in union, management and staff relations. During my time there, I was grateful to Betty Bannon, the taxation employee representative for PSAC and Marion Porrier of staff relations. This administrative background gave me an advantage when I later went to Yellowknife in the Northwest Territories as the Regional Occupational Health Nurse.

Over the next five years in the NWT, I worked with Dr. David Kinloch, the Regional Medical Health Officer, to establish the Federal Occupational Health Unit for the NWT. It quickly became apparent that a large part of my job would involve administering the employee assistance program, especially for federal employees in the remote communities. (The program we set up was effective, in spite of our not following the prescribed Ottawa format – we simply didn't have the personnel.) This work lasted until the Federal Government transferred health services to the Government of the Northwest Territories. Occupational Health, being a Treasury Board mandated program, was not transferable and the office was closed about a year later.

By that time, I was taking graduate level nursing courses at the University of Alaska in Anchorage. While there, I had the opportunity to travel with Circumpolar Health to the Russian Far East for two weeks. We visited hospitals, a reindeer camp with its own portable clinic, and a mining camp with a large medical facility. On my return to Canada, I transferred to Charlottetown, Prince Edward Island, to work for Veterans Affairs Canada. I worked there for five years until I had to come back home to Ontario.

This book has been a labour of love. As a northern nurse, I knew that hundreds of northern nurses' stories were untold. *Northern Nurses* collects some of these true and exciting adventures from Canada's North. Enjoy!

J. Karen Scott

FOREWORD

Seldom in the fast paced workplace do nurses have the opportunity to share their nursing memories that vividly colour their personal histories. The climate of the Canadian North has been the backdrop for experiences that have been etched in the memories of those nurses who have chosen to practise in this vast, sparsely populated land.

Jan Stirling, Yellowknife, NWT

* * *

The North is a very special place to live and work, and between the covers of this book, you will read stories, anecdotes and fragments from some exceptional people – mostly nurses – who have spent part, or all, of their lives there. They will tell you about their experiences, sometimes in very remote locations, and you will be amazed at the level of proficiency in the everyday practice of their profession. It should come as no surprise that two of our contributors, Sr. Cecile Montpetit and Barbara Bromley, have been awarded the Order of Canada for their work in the North.

You will also meet two Community Health Representatives from the aboriginal community. The work of the CHRs in the nursing stations and health centres is invaluable. Winnie Greenland of Fort McPherson is one, who also worked as an interpreter for the nurses for many years. Another, Regina Pastion, worked initially as a volunteer at the Hay Lakes Nursing Station and later at the Health Centre in Assumption, Alberta. She still works there at age seventy-five.

Bill Murray provides another perspective. As an environmental health officer who travelled the Inuvik Zone for a few years, Bill was always welcome in the stations. He knew how to help out in the kitchen – a hard lesson for many visitors (including doctors) was finding that they were judged more by their kitchen skills than by their professional expertise.

Some of the stories in this volume are fragments of the writers' overall time in the North, yet they stand out because of their humour, excitement, or drama. Other pieces tell us about the authors' lives over many years in the North and how that experience has changed them forever. Also included are stories of the daily (but rarely dull) work, which goes on in a nursing station that operates as a 24-hour walk-in clinic.

Each day in the station or health centre is different. As there are usually no appointments made, nurses don't know what problems they have to contend with until they walk into the treatment room, or answer the phone in the middle of the night. They could treat standard coughs and colds, or conduct follow-up visits from people on the Chronic List, which every station keeps for such diseases as TB and diabetes. Then there are the pre- and postnatals, and if there is a birthing centre, all the low-risk deliveries. Even when the station is not mandated to do deliveries, Nature may override *the* policy manual, at which point improvisation is needed, such as an incubator made out of spare parts. The nurse and the CHR regularly go out to the homes of mothers with newborns and at the same time, they review the immunization status of the other young children in the family. They also visit the elderly to check on their medications and overall well-being.

Nurses in the North often work on their own. But if they are lucky, there will be another nurse or if they are really lucky, there will be a doctor in residence. They may have to deal with snowmobile accidents, gunshot wounds and comas – situations that would normally require an emergency or intensive care unit. In the event of having to wait for the medical evacuation of a patient, due to weather conditions or the distance the medivac team has to travel, nurses must rely on their own skill and expertise with the assistance of a telephone link to the nearest hospital.

And as every nurse knows, there is that famous line in the job description: "…and other related duties." The nurse may be a mentor for young nurses, the trainer for new visiting doctors, or the undertaker. She, or he, may have to be the dentist, orthopaedic specialist, pediatrician, psychologist, radiologist, social worker, youth counsellor or sex educator. Whatever is required when a specialist is not at the station, *the nurse is it*. That could even include substituting, when necessary, for the veterinarian, the plumber, or the furnace repairperson. To handle night calls without an interpreter, nurses may need to master basic local language skills as well.

Because everyone lives and dies by the weather in the North, nurses, too, must have a constant awareness of it. They often develop an uncanny instinct for reading the skies. But sometimes, all they have to do is check the thermometer to know that nothing is flying, even though they need a medivac. They quickly learn to understand the implications of the pilot's announcement that ice fog has everything grounded. They realize how vital it is to know if the ice road is open, whether the ice bridge is in or out, and what the condition of the runway is.

During my years in the North, I noticed that the nurses who lasted the longest were those who got enough sleep. For them, medical problems were usually brought to the station during clinic hours and not in the middle of the night. In a real emergency – and there were many – nurses were always up and dressed in a flash, and into the clinic. It was sleep deprivation, especially during flu epidemics, that wore nurses down more than anything else. Those who were well-rested were the ones who were able to socialize in the community and enjoy the culture of their working environment. They had the time and energy to learn from the native people. One wise zone nursing officer used to encourage nurses to start planning their next vacation as soon as they returned from holidays. Knowing there was a scheduled break ahead helped relieve stress.

The RCMP played an important role in the North, especially if a nurse was on her own when things started to get out of hand. For her own safety, a nurse was instructed never to go to a home alone if she suspected that alcohol was involved. If an interpreter or another nurse was not available, standard procedure was to ask an officer to accompany her. The RCMP, "The Bay Boys," and the pilots were only a phone call away, and they were always right there. Their help was much appreciated by the nurses.

I often told the young nurses who came to my occupational health office as part of their orientation to the Zones, "Just remember, you will never be a normal nurse again after this experience. You will do procedures, and acquire nursing and medical knowledge that you were never taught in college or university, and you will discover that you are far more capable and competent than you ever dreamed. When you return home, you will find it almost impossible to cope within the limited range of duties allowed in southern hospitals." Perhaps that is why northern nurses keep going back for more – but more likely it is for the sense of independence they acquire, and the adventures they experience, and the satisfaction of conquering seemingly impossible situations.

J. Karen Scott

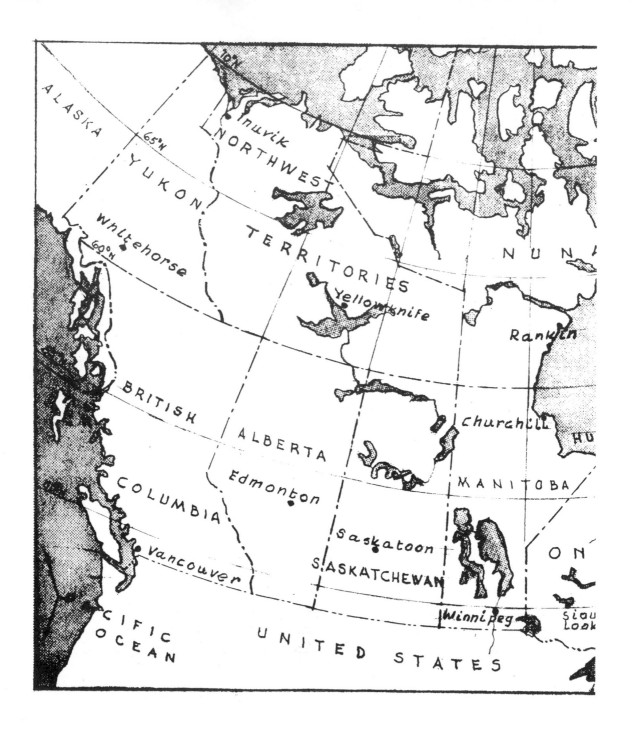

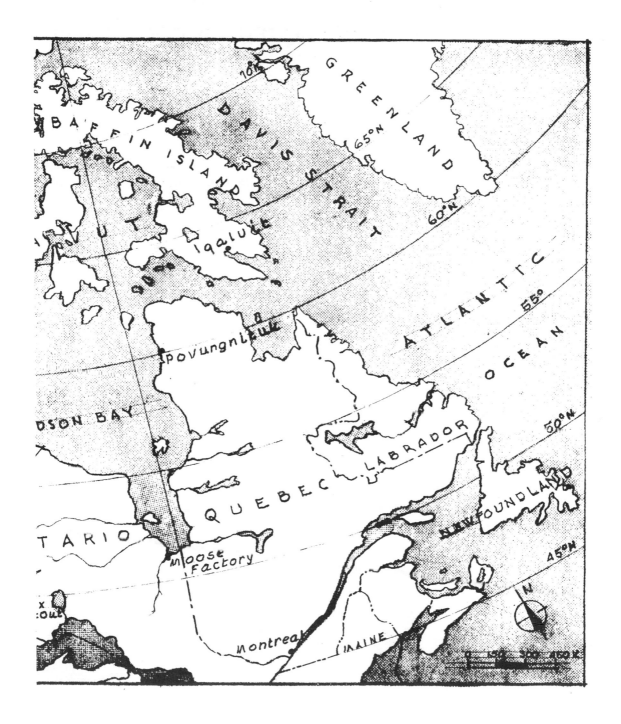

PREFACE TO THE SECOND EDITION

Many professionals have delivered pivotally important health services to people in remote areas of Canada, beginning in the 1600s and increasing by the mid-to-late 1800s. Of these, very few nurses or others have written stories about their experiences and about the conditions in which they worked. Fewer still have had their stories published in book form. Thus, *Northern Nurses: True Nursing Adventures from Canada's North* is a rarity. It constitutes an important contribution to the history of health care in Canada and is a tribute to the personal commitment, and sometimes heroism, of the remarkable people who serve in the North.

This unprecedented book is highly significant for a wide range of readers such as health services policy and priority makers and professional nursing associations who define the roles of nurses in primary health care, including their new "expanded role." It is also a unique resource for nursing, medical and other health care educators who help students understand the essence of "nursing practice." And it is an unparalleled reference for nurse historians and other historical researchers who need to find "real life" documented examples of how health professionals and others provide health care to people in isolated communities, often under extremely difficult circumstances. *Northern Nurses* is of great relevance to nurses and other professionals, including members of the Royal Canadian Mounted Police, who are thinking about the kinds of experiences they might face if they were to "go North," and it is also of interest to those who have recently been appointed to work in remote areas.

These stories have a significance which extends beyond the North. Nurse historian Dr. Jenny Klotz, as part of her doctoral research on "outback" nursing in Australia, visited nursing stations in Canada's North. Comparing practices in both locations, she said, "The essence of remote area nursing is the same – whether it be sand or snow!"

It is with great admiration and respect that I congratulate the authors for writing these stories and the editors of this book for putting them into print for the rest of us to learn from – and enjoy. As an old Chinese saying reminds us, "The palest of ink is better than the most retentive memory."

Shirley Stinson OC, AOE, RN, EdD, LLD (Hon), DSc (Hon)
Professor Emerita
Faculty of Nursing and Dept. of Public Health Services
University of Alberta
Edmonton, Alberta, T6G 2G3
July 2002

CONTENTS

NORTHERN IMMERSION

Robert Postma RN

The night began calm enough. A slight breeze was blowing from the west and the sun warmed the early spring evening, as we rested on the bank above the mighty Slave River in the Northwest Territories. Long shadows filtered through the trees as the sounds of birds complemented the roar of the Rapids of the Drowned and I reflected upon my current position. For you see, I had just graduated from school and had made the decision to head north, thereby fulfilling a dream that had burned in me for many years. Thinking about how fortunate I was to land a job so quickly made me smile. My night was only just beginning.

This evening was different from others, considering that I was on call for the very first time in my nursing career. In my mind was the thought, "What could go wrong? This pager has not gone off yet; I am living free and easy." Going back to my book, I tried to read. Instead I closed my eyes and inhaled the sweet spring air.

Then it happened. A high-pitched beeping at my hip broke the idyllic silence. For a moment, I could not figure out where the sound was coming from, and then it dawned on me that it came from my hip. While a message came across telling me to call the health centre as quickly as possible, I stayed there looking at the speaking piece of plastic in my hand. Dumbfounded, I realized I was not near a phone; but as my truck was handy, driving there would be quicker. Hopping in and speeding to the health centre, I kept hearing that same message repeating itself. Either they were joking around with me because I was "green," or a serious situation was brewing. When I arrived at the centre, I found the parking lot relatively empty. A joke then, I decided.

With a smile on my face, I sauntered down the main hallway where I was met by the nurse-in-charge, who informed me that there had been a plane crash outside of town and that the Search and Rescue technicians were bringing in two casualties. For the second time that night, my mind went blank; only this time it went numb as well. Now I considered myself knowledgeable coming out of school (and I was) but nothing quite prepared me for that evening. I managed to mumble that I really had no idea what to do. My colleague smiled as she told me to watch her and follow her lead: just keep my head about me and not panic.

The hospital quickly became a flurry of activity as the doctors (yes, we were lucky enough to have doctors), nurses and ambulance personnel arrived. I stood in a corner, out of the way, and watched as the action unfolded around me, maintaining my composure and my mind. After four hours, the patients were stabilized enough to be transferred south to a larger hospital, a trip that had to be taken on a small aircraft through a windstorm, the same windstorm that had allegedly caused the original plane to crash. This was a source of concern for me and the other occupants of the medivac. But all went well and we arrived home fourteen hours after having been called in to help.

I learned two lessons that night. The first – not to panic – has stayed with me for the last four years and has been an invaluable lesson, perhaps one of the greatest. The other lesson is that you must be prepared for anything that happens to come in through the front doors. Approach it all in the same manner: calm, confident, and with a sense of humour. There is a funny story in everything and everyone you meet "north of sixty." Realize it and laugh out loud about it later. And by the way, I did follow the lead of the nurse-in-charge. I gained a real sense of confidence and took part in the care of two seriously injured patients who both made a full recovery.

Robert Postma graduated from Fanshawe College in London, Ontario in 1996. He presently resides in Old Crow and says his Northern Immersion provided a steep learning curve for him.

A STUDENT NURSE IN LANSDOWNE HOUSE

Chantelle Dunlop BScN

The first time I landed at the airport in Lansdowne House in northern Ontario was after a very long and bumpy ride in a 10-seater plane. The airstrip was made of mud, which, luckily for me, was hard because the ground was frozen. If it is too soft, the plane will not land. The airport consisted of one room and a washroom with a toilet that did not work.

Rose Scrivens, the nurse to whom I was assigned, met me and took me first to the general store. Although it was only about the size of a large classroom, it supplied the food, clothing, hardware, health and sanitary needs of a community of about 350 people. I couldn't help but notice that the freshest foods available were a couple of wrinkled limes. Even though the temperature was only about 5-7°C, a young girl shopping with her mother was wearing her bathing suit and a pair of sweat pants. I could already tell this was going to be a different experience.

As Rose and I headed to what was to become my home for the next six weeks, I could see that Lansdowne house was very unlike southern Ontario. There were only dirt roads here, and the houses were tiny, many of them consisting of only a single room with no running water. This was typical of the "old" side of the reserve. The community was in the process of relocating to a new site where there was better land. At the time I was there, about half of the population lived on the new side where the school, arena, community centre and nursing station were located. This new side looked much like your typical subdivision, except there was no landscaping, and you were surrounded by a deep, sparkling blue lake and never-ending pine trees. At the present time, the community is still in the early stages of development. They have recently started taking leadership roles to determine the direction that growth should take. In fact, Lansdowne House received official reserve status just a few days before I left. The new reserve is named Neskantaga.

My impression was that the community took very little responsibility for its own health and was extremely reliant on the nurses whom they viewed as authority figures. It is sad to witness the degree of cultural loss that aboriginal peoples have experienced, especially in the areas of healing. Non-native culture is just beginning to recognize the broader definition of healing that includes more than science and medicine. We are starting to understand the importance of the native philosophy of health and healing which encompasses the body, mind and spirit, and the use of natural remedies. Meanwhile, isolated aboriginal communities in northern Canada are solely dependent on non-native nurses for western medicine. To me, this is a sad irony. This dependency makes the nursing role a demanding one.

The nurses are responsible for providing clinical care (including emergencies and prescribing medications), preventive care, health education and promotion. While I was there, I saw a great need for such education. I tried to bridge that gap by teaching in the schools, from grades three through eight, twice a week. As well, I worked on committees with local people to plan and carry out these teaching objectives.

I also participated in all other areas of nursing and found the experience challenging and fulfilling. Under Rose's supervision, I was privileged to be involved in many aspects of my profession, which never would have been allowed in a more conventional clinical setting in the South. I learned about native culture, and how history and politics have influenced the current state of aboriginal health in Canada. Along with that, I became familiar with a different way of life, which helped me to examine my own values and beliefs. The whole experience has affected me deeply.

Although I was anxious to return home to friends and family, I was sorry to leave and often, I have tugging thoughts of Lansdowne House. I have left a small piece of myself there, and it is waiting for me to return for it someday.

* * *

At the time that I am writing this, I am doing my fourth year clinical placement at The Hospital for Sick Children in Toronto. Not long ago, I had just completed my first shift on a cardiac floor. At report in the morning, a nurse mentioned that the three-year-old girl I would be providing care for could not speak English, but her parents could. I walked into the room expecting to see a family of a minority group I was familiar with in the Toronto area. To my surprise, it was a Cree family from an isolated reserve north of Winnipeg. I shared my experiences with them, and we were able to relate very well throughout the day. It caused me to reflect yet again on the impact that the outpost experience has had on my nursing practice, and on me personally. It revived many fond memories and gave me added inspiration to return some day.

Prior to her graduation in 1998 with a BScN from McMaster University in Hamilton, Ontario, *Chantelle Dunlop* spent six weeks at Lansdowne House. She has worked at an International Sports Camp in the Swiss Alps. In order to gain more clinical experience, she worked at The Hospital for Sick Children in Toronto on the Cardiac Unit. Chantelle now works at Cat Lake, Ontario. She is interested in pediatric and emergency nursing, and in health care politics.

MY LIFE AS A NORTHERN "UNDERFILL"

Karen Stauffer BSc, CIS
(Originally RN, CHN III)

Between 1980 and 1994, I spent almost ten years in the NWT and what is now Nunavut. Some of those years were as a hospital nurse, some as a community health nurse, and some as a stay-at-home mom. I have met many amazing nurses who had nursing degrees, midwifery diplomas and outpost nurses' training, and who were often far more experienced and more qualified than the doctors who came for their infrequent visits. Most had a very strong vision of nursing in the North – they relished the hardship and the challenge. I was not one of them. I just happened to meet and marry an RCMP officer, and after that my life was never the same. My story goes like this:

When I was growing up, my mother was a nurse and I had always wanted to be a nurse. I was only sixteen when I graduated from high school and more interested in partying than I was in settling down to serious studying, so I picked away at my nurse's training. First I did a one-year program to become a certified nursing assistant. I worked at that briefly, before I went back to school to get a certificate as an operating room technician. I tried that for a year and a half, until I took the plunge and returned to school to become a full-fledged registered nurse.

After I received my nursing diploma, I went back to work in the operating room. One evening, I was in a bar with a co-worker, bemoaning the fact that life was so "tough" for a 22-year-old O.R. nurse. My friend told me she had heard that northern nurses were flown in to work in Inuvik for three weeks and then out for three weeks' vacation. The more the night wore on, the better that began to sound. We checked into the possibility the next day. After finding out that getting hired into a federal nursing position required a lot of time and red tape, we called the personnel department at Stanton Yellowknife Hospital. Two weeks later (in February, 1980), my friend, Linda, and I found ourselves feeling quite dazed as we arrived in Yellowknife in our new fur coats and high-heeled boots. It was bitterly cold, and of course, there were no "three weeks in, three weeks out" jobs in existence. The last thing my mother had said to me as she put me on the plane in Saskatoon was, "Now don't you go and get married up there."

I started work on the medical ward, which also included psychiatry and the intensive care unit. One of the more exciting jobs was accompanying patients who required air ambulance (medivac) to Edmonton. One May evening, I received a call from the supervisor asking me if I would like to go on a medivac with two psychotic patients and their RCMP escorts. I was willing and soon found myself facing a four-hour flight in a Twin Otter with two RCMP officers and two patients on stretchers, swaddled in straight jackets and sleeping bags (the patients, not the

RCMP). The most memorable part of that trip was that one of the RCMP members (Scott) asked me out for the following evening, and then broke our date the next day because he was being posted temporarily to Snowdrift. (Snowdrift, now called Lutselk'e, is situated on the East Arm of Great Slave Lake, about 100 air miles straight east of Yellowknife.) Once Scott returned, though, he called again.

* * *

Less than a year later, we had our wedding date set. About six weeks before we were to be married, Scott was playing hockey on a team that included the RCMP commanding officer (who liked to be called "Corporal Bob" during hockey). While in the dressing room, "Corporal Bob" told Scott that he'd heard that he was marrying a nurse and asked him if he would like to be posted to Snowdrift. Scott said, "Sure!" A couple of days later, while still trying to digest that news, I received a call from the nursing officer at Northern Health. She had learned through the grapevine that we were moving to Snowdrift and was offering me a job as the second nurse. (The job was also very flatteringly called an "underfill position" because I didn't meet the qualifications for the job.) Two weeks after our wedding and a month short of my twenty-fourth birthday, we were moved to Snowdrift by RCMP Twin Otter, with all of our new wedding gifts, to start out our married life and our new positions.

When I began working at Snowdrift, I felt adventuresome and full of bravado (so much so, that I could see that the regional nursing officers were not sure what they thought of me during the orientation week). I also felt very young and inexperienced. I had a full month with one of the most experienced settlement nurses in the NWT, before she moved on. Then a series of temporary nurses came in to relieve the nurse-in-charge position (or not) until a permanent nurse-in-charge, Marilyn Mooney, was finally hired eight months later. I soon had to face reality and get down to work, many times on my own. I found the people in the community very friendly and helpful. Two local employees at the nursing station: a janitor and a housekeeper, who also doubled as interpreters, were invaluable for filling me in on past histories and home situations.

As green as I felt as a settlement nurse, I discovered that I had more knowledge and intuition than I ever would have imagined. I was, for the most part, able to meet the challenges that occur for any nurse in an isolated posting. I discovered that I had a much-needed skill in suturing from my years in the O.R., as well as experience doing pelvic exams, drawing blood and inserting IVs. The many varied experiences from my one and half years spent on the medical ward in Yellowknife had also helped to prepare me for this job. But I also spent many hours reading the medical texts available there, and talking on the phone with the medical and nursing contacts I had made in Yellowknife.

So, in the company of Marilyn, the nurse-in-charge, or sometimes on my own, I faced the constant variety of everyday and not so common medical problems, admitting or medivac'ing patients as needed, trying to keep up with the immunizations and the TB recalls. It was an enormous growing experience for me. Often my work overlapped with my husband's, and occasionally it involved critical illnesses or severe injuries. The stories that stand out in my memory, however, are not about the times that we daringly saved lives or delivered babies. (Actually, I would do just about anything to avoid a delivery – luckily Marilyn was a British-trained midwife and I somehow managed to avoid having to do one while I was on my own. That was likely a good thing, because although I had assisted with numerous births, they were all Caesarian sections in the operating room.)

* * *

One time, a woman came in to the nursing station with her new dentures. She showed me how they were too big and slipped around in her mouth. I remembered that in the storeroom we had some denture adhesive, which I promptly went and retrieved. I helped her to apply it and then helped insert the dentures. They now no longer slipped off, but they really were too large for her mouth. The poor woman started to gag. She tried to remove them and I tried to remove them but they were stuck and weren't coming off. I was the sole nurse in the community at that time, and the waiting room was filling up. While I put in a call to a dentist, I had the woman wait outside where she stood on the steps and gagged over the railing. Everybody kept coming in and telling me about her. Finally the dentist called back, and between guffaws, gave me the instructions on how to break the seal on her dentures so we could get them out of her mouth. That lady was so appreciative – I don't know why, as she should have been very annoyed.

* * *

As part of the school program, I set out to teach sex education to the teenagers. Because the Catholic Church ran the school at that time, we had to go to the priest and the school board to get permission (even though the rate of teen pregnancies was sky high). They allowed the program but said it was to be taught at the nursing station, and that boys and girls were to be taught separately. The only space in the station large enough to seat a group and show films was the storeroom, so that was where I conducted the classes. A couple of days after the boys' first class, a young teenager came into the nursing station to see me. He was very shy and said one word: "rubber." I was so pleased that my teaching had sunk in. I chattered away as I filled a small paper bag with condoms and handed it to the boy. He looked in the paper bag and then at me, and said, "No, I meant rubber tubing for slingshots." He had seen it in the storeroom while he was in the class.

* * *

Marilyn and I were particularly keen on participating in community life. One Halloween, we decided to go to the community dance and we dressed up like flowers, with green garbage bag leaves and paper petals around our faces. At the advertised time, we both showed up at the hall; but everything was dark and locked up, so we headed home.

The following day, I found out from the housekeeper that the dance had been postponed. Somehow, Marilyn and I were the only ones who hadn't known that. The next night, we returned to the hall to find the dance in full swing. We had a lively time, since all of the teenaged boys, who were so painfully shy when they came to the nursing station, were very outgoing while they wore masks. Both of us were kept going on the dance floor, as one teenager after the other asked us to dance!

* * *

During my second year in Snowdrift, I decided to run in the elections for the Co-op board and was voted in. At my first meeting, I sat feeling rather uncomfortable because the proceedings were in Chipewyan and because the group kept looking at me. I could catch the odd word, and kept hearing them say, "Nurse." I thought, "Uh-oh, they're going to ask me to leave." To my surprise, the manager finally turned to me and announced, "You're the president." After that meeting, I insisted on having someone interpret for me.

Because of the upgrading training I received through Health and Welfare Canada (so I would no longer be an "underfill"), I had many opportunities to interview the elders and listen to their stories about traditional medicine and midwifery. One elderly woman talked about her method of delivering babies, with the mother kneeling on a cushion and pulling on handles made from a caribou skin stretched across a pole. I also heard stories about hunting for caribou with canoes and spears, and hunting for musk ox on the barren lands, and I listened to tales of disease and starvation. It was incredible to talk to people who remembered the days when tents were made of caribou skin – when their lives were totally nomadic and dependent on the land.

Scott and I left Snowdrift after two years. Before I went, I sold my high-heeled boots in a garage sale, hoping and praying the young girl who bought them wouldn't break her ankle wearing them on the uneven gravel roads. We were next posted to Rankin Inlet. From there, we moved to Alberta for four years and then we returned to the NWT for another six years.

* * *

Looking back, I realize that although there was poverty, alcoholism, and family violence up North, I certainly don't dwell on that, because I know that I don't have to look very far in my present "southern" city to find the same thing. What remains for me are memories of the amazing beauty of the land, the breath-taking sunsets (when there was sun), and the Saturdays spent fishing with my husband. I also remember the many people that I felt I knew so well for that short time. I admired the young women for their beauty and pride – they were such loving moms and had such strength and skill when it came to the things they needed to do in order to cope in that harsh land. I adored the old people for their dignity and graciousness, just as I did my grandmother, whom I considered to be next only to the queen.

I am no longer a nurse – although when I say that, most people respond with, "once a nurse, always a nurse." While we were living in Pond Inlet, I worked on my nursing degree through distance education and happened to take an optional computer class. I discovered a new love and completed an undergraduate degree in computer science. I now work as a programmer analyst, but I still look back at those northern nursing days with nostalgia and certainly no regret, for the incredible privilege of living and working in the North.

Karen Stauffer was born and raised in Biggar, Saskatchewan. While pursuing her nursing education at the Kelsey Institute in Saskatoon and the Wascana Institute in Regina, she qualified as a Certified Nursing Assistant in 1974, an Operating Room Technician in 1976 and a Registered Nurse in 1979. In June 1998, Karen graduated from Athabasca University with a BSc in Computing and Information Systems and has been working for Athabasca University as a programmer analyst since then. Her husband, who is still in the RCMP, is now a Staff Sergeant. They have made Fort McMurray their home since leaving the NWT in 1994.

TRAVELLING IN THE INUVIK ZONE: AN EHO'S PERSPECTIVE

Bill Murray CPHI (C)

In 1985, I joined the Medical Services team and took a posting in Inuvik in the Northwest Territories. Along with all the other medical staff, I was immediately inducted into the "ice worms," an initiation rite which anyone who has worked at the Inuvik General Hospital will know about. Occasionally, when I am in an off-the-wall mood, I wear the T-shirt I received that evening.

As an environmental health officer, I was responsible for the environmental health programmes in the communities of Inuvik, Aklavik, Fort McPherson, Sachs Harbour, Paulatuk, and Tuktoyaktuk. Regular monthly visits to these communities, either by air or by road (ice road in the winter for Tuktoyaktuk), entailed staying over for at least one night in the medical services facility. This might be a trailer, a cabin, or space in the nursing station.

Because I was involved in public health issues such as food poisoning (including botulism), rabies contacts, VD investigations (male only), water-related illness, communicable disease control, occupational health problems and various other health-related issues, I often worked with the local nurses. This was always a bonus as these men and women were a pleasure to work with. During my stay, I was frequently invited for lunch or supper, and invariably, I felt welcome. Conversation would stray from public health matters to the local point of interest and eventually to personal problems and concerns.

My discussions with all the medical services staff during my visits to the communities eventually led me into the Employee Assistance Programme where I was trained as a referral agent. The program was based in Yellowknife, out of the regional occupational health office. The isolation, and unusual occurrences to which the staff were often subjected, took its toll emotionally. I like to think I was a factor in assisting some good people in obtaining the help they needed to regain their dignity and remain in their chosen field.

On a lighter note, the quiet off hours spent with the nurses in the various communities will never be forgotten. Good conversation, jokes, excellent meals, companionship and a feeling of accomplishment will always be a fond memory for me.

I have great respect for the men and women who nurse in the Arctic or any other remote posting. These people give up their comfortable lives in modern cities, with all the amenities, to go to isolated post communities to help the northern people. The residents they help are unique in that they are often unfamiliar with the nurses' earlier lifestyle, before arriving in their village. As for the public health staff, they must learn the culture and traditions of the people. And in order to be effective in their new setting, they have to adapt the teaching techniques they have learned from the culture in the South. Each isolated community is different and has its own personality.

My wife worked as a registered practical nurse at the Inuvik Hospital, and my daughter, who is an RN, on several occasions, visited and did some medivacs. The three years we spent in the Arctic, probably the best in our lives, will never be forgotten. Since leaving, we have kept in touch with many of the nurses we met there. I found an Arctic "espris de corps" among the nurses, and I hope they included me in that.

After graduating from Ryerson University as a Certified Public Health Inspector, *Bill Murray* worked as an EHO at the St. Catherines and Muskoka-Parry Sound Health Units. In 1985, he joined the Medical Services Branch of Health Canada and moved to Inuvik with his wife Carole. He later transferred to the Thunder Bay Zone and the Sudbury office. He and Carole are now retired and enjoy travelling.

SHOOTOUT AT THE TUNDRA O.K. CORRAL

Lesley Singer RN, SCM

One of my most memorable experiences occurred in the late 1970s when I had been in a settlement only a few months. It was June, spring in the Northwest Territories, with twenty-four hour daylight. The sunshine was glorious, but the snow had hardly started to melt.

There had been a party, a drop-in affair, with people coming and going all evening and throughout the night. I had left in the early hours of the morning and returned to the nursing station. We had had a codaphone (a recording machine) installed at the nursing station and it was in use for the first time. The nurse-on-call, who was staying in the float nurse apartment, had left a message on the codaphone. Since no one in the community was familiar with how it worked, they ignored it. For the whole night, the nurse who should have been on duty remained peacefully at home in bed.

Shortly after I arrived back at the nursing station, we were notified that there had been a suicide. One of the nurses, who knew the family, went to the home to assist the RCMP and help the family deal with the tragedy. News travels fast in a small community, and soon everyone knew the sad news, including the people who had been at the party. Possibly this is what triggered the following events.

One of the partygoers who had heard what had happened was a gentleman with an alcohol problem. In the past he had been involved in a snowmobiling incident. He suffered from severe frostbite, making necessary a below-knee amputation on one leg and mid-foot amputation on the other. He took Valium intermittently for his phantom pains, and knowing the dangers of mixing Valium and alcohol, he was generally compliant. On this occasion, however, he had taken both and become confused. He went home and got his gun; but since he didn't have any ammunition, he went to The Bay, broke in, and stole a huge quantity. Initially, he went to his estranged wife's house, where he did a lot of damage. Then he wandered throughout the community, taking pot shots here and there. He stopped at The Bay manager's house for tea and to explain to him that he had broken into the store. After that, he went back outside and started shooting at the RCMP who were approaching him.

As soon as the RCMP got in touch with us, we phoned people to stay in their homes, to keep down below window level, and to sit tight until the RCMP caught the man. We prepared for an impending crisis because we thought that sooner or later somebody would get shot. We put the emergency equipment onto a trolley and ran with the trolley, around the nursing station from door to door, trying to decide where the accident was most likely to happen. We also made sure the emergency bag and stretcher were ready in case we had to go to the incident site.

In the meantime, the man with the gun had wandered past the government offices and had gone behind the nursing station. The RCMP followed him, and with more luck than judgment, he missed when he shot at one of the officers. He went up and over the rocks, situating himself at the rear of the station. We could tell where he was because he continued taking pot shots at anyone or anything he could see.

Eventually, the RCMP decided they needed more firepower. They asked us to phone around to several people in the community who were good shots, who would be calm in emergencies, and who would be prepared to assist. Most were elders. The group spread themselves around the rocks to see if someone could get the man to come out. In theory, someone would shoot him. In practice, no one was keen to do that.

Meanwhile, we were still running around the station with our emergency trolley, drinking tea, and otherwise enjoying the sun. Around 6:30 in the morning, one of the RCMP shot the man in the right hand. We were lucky, as we had expected some nasty gunshot injuries. They brought him in with his gun, which was wrecked. The shot had amputated two and a half fingers on his right hand, and he was in shock. Everyone breathed a sigh of relief as the community went back to normal. People went to bed and tried to calm down.

We bandaged his hand and got a plane; then I took him to Winnipeg with an RCMP escort. In November, five months after the incident happened, he came to trial, and was found guilty on a variety of charges. For our part, being witnesses and taking good notes immediately taught us a lot about trials.

After her training in Queen Alexandra's Royal Naval Nursing Service, *Lesley Singer* served in England and in Malta. She moved to Scotland to do midwifery, volunteering with the Air Medivac Service in her off-duty hours. From 1971 to 1974 Lesley worked in Zambia. Since 1975, she has nursed in the Canadian North. She worked in Labrador for three years before moving to the Northwest Territories. She is married to Garry Singer and they have two children.

DELIVERY BY FLASHLIGHT

Faye Stark RN, BA, BN

It was a dark night in February, 1974, in Pelican Narrows, Saskatchewan. I had been in the community for six months, a new graduate with no previous nursing experience. Around 2 a.m., two young fellows, about 12 and 10 years of age, arrived at the nursing station to tell me that their mother was having a baby. In those days, there were no roads to many of the houses, and the only vehicle that the nursing station had was a car. Because there was no road to this house, I gave the sons blankets and a sleeping bag to carry, while I brought the physician's large black delivery bag. We walked for about half a mile to their small log house.

Inside, I found a grandma sitting beside a labouring woman. It was cold, as the wood fire was out; so I woke up the husband to light it, which he did. When I examined the woman, I could tell that the birth was going to happen very soon. Because it was so cold, I left my parka on while I prepared the delivery site as best I could, taking care to keep the woman warm.

Almost at the crucial moment, an RCMP officer arrived at the door to say that there was a woman in labour in his truck. I raced outside to find a pregnant woman with abdominal pain; but quickly judging that her delivery was not imminent, I felt that she could wait a few minutes. That was a good thing because I could hear someone yelling, "Nurse!" from inside the house. With the RCMP at my heels, I ran back to the first woman in time to see the baby's head crowning. Since the kerosene lamp was not giving enough light for me to see, I yelled for the officer to shine his flashlight. Out popped a healthy boy who began to cry right away. I cut the cord, wrapped the baby in a blanket and gave him to the grandma to put inside her parka to keep him warm. The rest of the delivery proceeded without a problem.

After it was all over, the other family members woke up and cooed over the baby. The husband took a look and remarked, "Oh, it's a boy," and went back to bed. This was his fifth son and he had wanted a daughter. We bundled the patients into a taxi, and with me as their escort, drove to the nearest hospital, which was three hours away on a gravel road. The second prenatal was diagnosed with false labour and a urinary tract infection.

THE RCMP AMBULANCE DRIVER

In January, 1976, around 4 o'clock in the morning, a woman in active labour arrived at the nursing station in Pelican Narrows, Saskatchewan. At that time, the RCMP helped us to drive medical emergencies to the nearest hospital, which was about three hours away. We took off with the labouring woman and me in the back, and the officer driving. He was new to town and had been with the Force for only two years.

Every time the woman had a pain, she cried out. Every time she cried out, the RCMP officer's eyes grew wider and the car went faster and faster. When we were about half way to the hospital, speeding down the icy road at 60 mph, the gas pedal froze. We made every curve and turn all right, but I knew that we would soon be coming to a T-intersection outside of town, and would need to turn left. I also feared that, at this speed, we were not going to make it. Just as we approached the turn, the officer slammed the car into reverse. We stopped instantly. He calmly put the car into drive, the gas pedal unfroze, and we slowly drove the last ten miles to the hospital. Two hours later, the woman delivered a healthy baby.

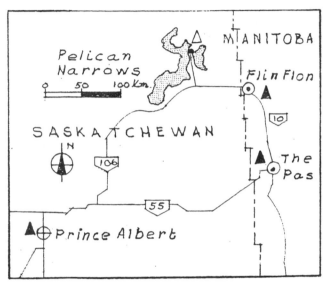

THE SWIM OF HIS LIFE

People still tell this story about an environmental health officer who used to come to Fort Providence in 1965. At that time, a new sewage lagoon had been built near the middle of town. Occasionally, it smelled bad. That summer, this EHO was sent to test the middle of the lagoon at various depths to see why it smelled like fresh sewage. He arrived with a special scoop at the end of a pole and inquired about borrowing a boat. Needless to say, people were not too helpful, for who in his right mind wanted his fishing boat stinking of raw sewage. After much asking around, he found someone who would sell him an older rowboat, for a small fee. He rowed it to the middle of the lagoon, and just as he was using his new scoop to get samples, the boat split apart, and the EHO ended up swimming in the lagoon. He managed to get out and walk back to the motel for a much needed shower. He didn't ask for another boat. The lagoon was promptly closed, and a new one was soon built away from town.

After graduating from Red Deer College with her RN in 1973, *Faye Stark* worked at the nursing station in Pelican Narrows, Saskatchewan. She obtained her BA, BN and Nurse Practitioner qualifications, and successfully completed studies in Advanced Practical Obstetrics. She worked in Little Grand Rapids, Grassy Narrows, Tuktoyaktuk, Norman Wells, Gjoa Haven, Fort Providence, Fort McPherson, Snowdrift, Yellowknife and Fort Simpson. She has worked as a community health nurse, nurse-in-charge, nurse educator with ANSEP and manager of health services. Faye has spent more than half her life in the North. Her husband Mac is manager of the Northern Store in Fort Providence.

ALONG THE LABRADOR COAST

Nancy Miller-Hardy RN, BScN, MScN

During my two and a half year stay with the International Grenfell Association in North West, Labrador, in the mid 1970s, we had an outbreak of diphtheria in Goose Bay and a forest fire that surrounded the village of North West River, which forced us to stay in boats out on the bay until it was put out. There was a plane crash that caused the death of two people and an incident in which I was left stranded in the middle of nowhere on a *komatik* (a sled) which had become unfastened from the snowmobile, unbeknownst to the station master who was driving me to another nursing station. One night, a disturbed resident of Black Tickle threatened to remove an injured dog from the nursing station without our consent. For most of the night, he circled the nursing station in his snowmobile, with a rifle on his back.

Throughout that time, I travelled the coast as the public health nursing supervisor working in conjunction with the Medical Officer of Health for Newfoundland and Labrador. In the past, the British had played a large part in providing medical services to this area, and having public health directed by Canadian personnel was a whole new experience for the Brits and the communities.

One day, while at the Hopedale Nursing Station, I received a call on the radio from a new British doctor who was stationed at the North West River Hospital. He asked me to attend to an emergency at the nursing station in Davis Inlet, Labrador. At that time, Davis Inlet had a population of about 250 people who continued to live in tents and whose only access to the outside world was by plane or boat, and snowmobiles in the winter.

According to a volunteer at the nursing station, a resident of Davis Inlet had brought in a wolf with the hope that the nurse would make it well. The volunteer saw the wolf frothing at the mouth and panicked. Rabies! After being given that information over the phone, the doctor advised the person to kill the wolf, cut off the head and place it in the freezer at the nursing station. He then radioed me, the closest one to this station and ordered me to pick up the head and take it to North West River where it would, in turn, be transported by another plane to a lab in St. John's, Newfoundland.

I tried to explain to the doctor that there had been no known cases of rabies in Labrador. To rule out a possible outbreak, he decided to send a special plane for me to pick up the head immediately. He also sent a lab coat and rubber gloves, and advised me to place the head carefully into a plastic bag. When I arrived on the shore of Davis Inlet, a line of very unhappy residents greeted me. They were not pleased with the aforementioned actions. They believed that the wolf was suffering from dehydration and only needed veterinary-type attention from the nurse.

On seeing their great displeasure, I thought that the best way to proceed was to put on my lab coat and look as official as possible, as I walked through the disgruntled group to the nursing station. By the time I returned to Paddon Hospital, it was too late for testing purposes, and the head had somehow disappeared into the basement. I wonder if anyone ever found that skull. It certainly had a story to tell.

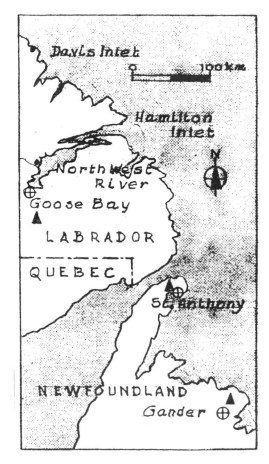

* * *

Life on the Labrador coast was not all work, and we took advantage of any opportunity to enjoy the lifestyle of the area. On one occasion, we went trout fishing by boat in early October. A storm dropped more than a foot of snow and forced us to go ashore quickly for our own safety. We were lucky that we had some supplies with us, including a tent in which we stayed overnight. Fortunately, there was a trapper's cabin close by which held the bare essentials such as flour and salt. Our friend, who had worked for the Wild Life Association, shot a Canada goose and we had Thanksgiving dinner early that year. It tasted *so* good!

* * *

Another experience I will never forget was the time I was honoured to be able to attend a seal-hunting venture in the spring of 1975 along with the residents of North West River. On our skidoos, pulling *komatiks*, we ventured out on the frozen bay. It was a beautiful day, and quite a sight to observe the skills of the hunters who were very respectful of their prey. The harp seal is used by the local people for a variety of purposes, providing food and warmth in the winter months. I still have seal skin mitts and mukluks.

We spent a full day hunting and killed three seals that were carried on the *komatiks*. In the evening, we ate one that was prepared over an open fire. I had the pleasure of eating seal liver, which has an unforgettable taste and a texture all its own. We kept warm in tents that were heated with stoves. The floors were lined with cedar boughs, and we used a bear rug for a cover. In the morning, after a hearty breakfast, we headed home with the heat of the sun on our backs.

There were three other *komatiks* in our party. As we were getting closer to home and near the shore, we heard the crew behind us holler for help. To our dismay, we saw the *komatik* start to descend into the ice of the bay. The passenger on it scrambled helplessly at the edge of the hole in the icy water. I don't know how he was able to survive the sub-zero temperatures. We were afraid to move an inch for fear that we would all fall into the bay. The Labradorians took all of this in their stride, calmly guiding the rest of us to safety. Although we lost the snowmobile, the *komatik* and one of our catches, fortunately, there were no human casualties.

My short stay in Labrador was indeed a once-in-a-lifetime adventure. I admire the people who continue to live in Canada's great North and I am grateful that I had a chance to share some of their experience.

Nancy Miller-Hardy graduated from Hamilton and District School of Nursing in Hamilton, Ontario in 1968. She completed her Diploma in Public Health in 1969 at the University of Windsor, Ontario, and in 1974 she graduated with a BScN from the University of British Columbia in Vancouver. She worked in Newfoundland and Labrador with The International Grenfell Association from 1974 to 1976. She was nursing supervisor at the Middlesex and London District Health Unit from 1976 to 1984 while completing her MScN at the University of Western Ontario. She taught nursing at Laurentian University in Sudbury, Ontario from 1984 to 1985. Nancy married in 1985 and lives in California where she is currently employed as a nurse specialist doing follow-up on high-risk infants and their families after discharge from the Neonatal Intensive Care Unit.

A NORTHERN NURSE FROM DOWN UNDER

Chris Siksik RN, RM

It was a sunny, cold day in January of 1969 when EJ, a fellow nurse, and I flew in to Rankin Inlet from Fort Churchill, Manitoba. As we circled overhead, we could see snowmobiles racing towards the airport. The land was barren and, in the middle of complete isolation, stood a collection of small houses. For two girls from evergreen New Zealand, this was a shock. Churchill at least had sparse trees and bush.

EJ and I had been working at the Fort Churchill Hospital and were to relieve at the Rankin Nursing Station, until they were able to find more permanent replacements for the two nurses who had just left. It would be an adventure, while at the same time quite scary, as neither of us had worked without the support of other medical staff before.

The nursing station was made up of three trailers in the form of a rather lopsided H. One trailer was our clinic; the middle section contained the entrance and all the stores for the clinic; the comfortable living quarters were in the third. The local hotel, Siniktarvik, was close by, and it was just a short walk down to The Bay, the only store in the community.

By the first Saturday, we were ready to go to the weekly square dance where Annie, our interpreter, gave us a running commentary on all the people. After Arsene (an Inuk whom I would later marry) arrived with two of the schoolteachers who were our age, we soon joined the group and enjoyed the night learning to square dance. We also made friends with "The Bay Boys," Alan and Peter. "The Bunk House" of The Bay seemed to be the hub of the young peoples' entertainment, so we spent much of our off time there. In those days, in a community of 680, you did not need beepers, as everyone knew where you were if there was an emergency.

EJ and I managed the clinic without too many hiccups. A most exciting time was our one and only birth. The mother, who was from Baker Lake, had been on her way to Churchill. There had been a storm, and as this was the first plane out in several days, it was overbooked. Someone had created a fuss, and it happened that the woman (who, incidentally, had omitted to explain that she was in early labour and actually should be going straight to Churchill) was bumped. By the time she arrived at the station, she was in full labour. While this was baby number 13 for her, neither EJ nor I had done a delivery on our own. I had been the "baby catcher" at five deliveries in my training, which was more than EJ had done. We both knew that there was a risk of bleeding. Fortunately, we did not have to put in an IV. She had an easy birth, and delivered a lovely, healthy baby. I should add that I now have twenty years of midwifery experience, and EJ runs a very large neonatal unit in Sioux Falls, South Dakota.

After almost eight weeks in Rankin, it was time for us to go back to Fort Churchill, as the new nurses were due to arrive. We still had one surprise left for us, when we found out that Annie, our interpreter, was pregnant (those observant nurses hadn't even noticed) and so our last job was to get Annie out to Churchill in time to have her baby.

* * *

Within a few months, Arsene and I were on our way to Auckland where we were married on January 10, 1970. He completed his apprenticeship in plumbing, but felt a bit uncomfortable being the only Inuk in New Zealand. In 1972, I received my diploma in midwifery, which I trusted would improve my future chances of working in the North. Our first son, Alex, was born in 1973, and in 1974, we returned to Rankin hoping to find work. Although we could both get jobs, there was no housing available; so we moved on to Churchill for a short time. After that, it was back to Auckland where our second son, Paul, was born in 1976.

In 1979, we again headed to the North while the boys were still young enough so that it would not interfere with their schooling. We had both arranged for jobs and housing in Rankin. Here I was, back at the nursing station, ten years later. Many changes had been made since I had left, with the station having moved across the road into a much larger, well-equipped facility. The place was still divided into three sections with living quarters, clinic, and storage areas. There were four nurses working full-time, all having different areas of expertise, which made for a good team. We also had support staff from clerk/interpreters to cleaners and general workers. By now, Rankin had grown to around 1200 people.

Pat and I, being the married nurses on staff, lived with our families in apartments within the community, while Lesley and June-Anne lived in the nursing station. When we were on call with in-patients, we would stay at the station; otherwise, we would come in from home to meet our patients there.

Around this time, Arsene and I had been planning to have child number three, and shortly after our arrival in Rankin, we found that I was pregnant. I ended up in Thompson about three weeks before the due date, eating my way through the fresh baked bread and the selection of fresh vegetables available in the shops. I realized what it was like for all the women, who for health reasons, were not eligible to deliver in Rankin and had to be away from family during such an important time. Arsene, who had taken holidays, arrived about one week before I was due, bringing Alex and Paul with him. They were scheduled to leave, but after some crying to the obstetrician, I was induced and Stuart, son number three, was born.

For almost four more years, we stayed on in Rankin with me relieving periodically at the station and doing the odd medivac and Arsene working for the Department of Public Works. We became good friends with a couple whose two elder children were the same age as our older two. Cathy, the other mother, and I decided to set up shop selling crafts. I also taught at Maani

Ulujuk School, as they did not have a music teacher at that time. I really enjoyed introducing the kids to Raffi and his music, and even taught them a Maori *poi* song, getting them to make pois so they could do the actions as well. A *poi* is a Maori flax ball tied on the end of a string and swung in time to the singing. It was rewarding to hear one of my ex-pupils still able to sing the song to me, fifteen years later.

* * *

In August of 1983, son number one, Alex, needed to be home in Auckland for junior high school; for that reason, it was back to New Zealand, once more leaving behind family and friends. After we had stayed there for fifteen years, we decided that the two older boys were independent enough for us to return to Rankin for an extended period of time. We packed up, sold our car and left the house in the tender care of the two boys, taking Stuart with us, knowing he would have a chance to finish his education in Rankin, which now had a high school.

Determined not to land there in the dead of winter this time, we scheduled our arrival for August of 1998. I would be working at the birthing centre in Rankin, as the two midwives were leaving two weeks after my arrival. The airport was full of family to greet us. And what a modern airport it was! Rankin now had a population of 2700. We were assigned a three-bedroom apartment with a wonderful view of the bay, in a relatively quiet area about a five-minute walk from the centre of town.

On my first Monday in Rankin, I reached the health centre a little after 8:30, having first gone with my son to see him settled in school and to discuss his New Zealand qualifications. When I walked in on the morning meeting, I found there was a huge number of staff compared to what I was previously used to at the nursing station. The place was also drastically changed, as we were now meeting in what were once the living quarters. I was introduced to everyone and then it was back to the day's agenda to discuss what had happened in the previous night's call and what we could expect for the day.

* * *

I met Wendy, a registered nurse with obstetric experience, who was going to be the stand-in for the second midwife. I had not realized that I would be the only midwife. Wendy had arrived only a short time before me, and so both of us took some time to get orientated to the routine. Running a birthing centre, with all the continuity of care it involved, was a new experience for me. During the second week, we had three deliveries. It was a real pleasure to care for the Inuit women who overall had the calmest and easiest labour and birth experiences.

Nowyah Williams, who had been with the birthing centre for the five years since it had been open and was a very skilled obstetrical nurse, had gone out to Ottawa to complete a Registered Nursing Assistant course. The fact that Nowyah took care of her own patients, under the supervision of one of the midwives, lightened our load.

The Rankin Inlet Birthing Centre is the only facility of its kind in the NWT and Nunavut. It opened due to political pressure from the Inuit mothers. They wanted to have their babies in the community and not be sent south for several weeks, leaving their families behind as they waited for confinement. Here, each mother was to be followed throughout her pregnancy by one nurse. Her case was reviewed by the OBS Committee at sixteen and thirty-four weeks gestation to determine suitability for delivering at the centre. Only low risk mothers were eligible for delivery in Rankin. In the centre, we saw prenatal patients in the morning and a mix of pre- and postnatals in the afternoons. Home visits were done daily for several days following delivery regardless of the weather. Newborns were followed at home for six weeks by the birthing centre staff and then transferred to public health and the health centre for routine and sick visits.

The hardest thing for me was dealing with medical people who did not really understand the midwife's role. They did not see us as being any different from the regular nursing staff. At one of our morning meetings, we were told that there would be no deliveries while there was no doctor in Rankin, even though the birthing centre was never created to be "doctor dependent." There were many heated comments over that decision. When one of the nurses who had planned to deliver at the centre was due, she decided that, doctor or no doctor, she was staying in Rankin to have her baby. There was some risk involved as she was a primigravida, but she was willing to take that chance and ended up having an uneventful delivery at the birthing centre with all her family around for support.

In mid-January of 1999, Wendy, the other RN, decided to leave Rankin, which meant that Nowyah and I were on our own. As management had been looking for another midwife, without much success, I contacted a friend on the Internet and put out a call for help. A midwife from Ontario, who had previously worked at Povungnituk in northern Quebec, joined us. Another midwife, who had been working at St. Boniface in Winnipeg, took time off to come north and help us.

It was wonderful to have other midwives to share the responsibility and the on-call time. They each brought a new dimension to Rankin, and each added a little of her own personality to midwifery. Sari Fogg, who was originally from Spain, had done her general training in Canada and had gone to England to do her midwifery training. She was involved in setting up midwifery in Manitoba. They both stayed a relatively short period of time, and then it was back to being on my own with Nowyah and using health centre nurses to help with the birthings.

We had been looking into the idea of setting up a course to train midwives from the local population. Povungnituk had already trained Inuit midwives. We had an opportunity to go to Inukjuak, south of POV, where they were expanding the program and were in the process of training two more Inuit midwives. Quebec had also become one of the provinces that recognized midwives and had a College of Midwifery. They accepted the qualifications of the

POV midwives, with the restriction that they would only be able to practise within northern communities.

During this time, Sue Pauhl (a voice from the past for me, as she had taken over from Pat Cluderay as head nurse at Rankin Inlet while we were there in the early 1980s) and Johanna Verraci, another experienced nurse, came to fill in at the centre. I was able to attend the Midwifery Alliance of North America Conference at Lake Tahoe and present a paper on the Rankin Birthing Centre and the training of Inuit Midwives. I was proud to do this, since my great grandmother had been a midwife in the 1800s in New Zealand where midwifery had always been part of obstetrics.

* * *

The community of Rankin had changed dramatically from the way it was during my second time there in 1983. We now had two supermarkets with a great range of goods. The hotel, Siniktarvik, had expanded. We had restaurants and a coffee shop, two banks, two large apartment buildings and several sizeable office buildings. There were now three schools well-staffed with local teachers and some from the South. A big arena had been built, complete with a hall, a skating and curling rink. However, along with the expansion and growth, came all the same social problems found in the South; but here they seemed to be greatly increased in number and severity. The result was a lot of sadness and difficulty for many families.

By the end of 1999, I went out to Winnipeg for a break, to meet my sons who were arriving from New Zealand for a visit. Nuri Sinuff and Barb Lashley came in to help, as I had been on my own for some time. Nuri had been around the North for many years, having worked in Arviat and Sanikiluaq. She had come north during a period when nurses with midwifery qualifications were doing all the low-risk births at the stations. Both gave me support at a time when I most needed it. I will always be grateful to them. With more staff in the birthing centre, I was able to spend time out on the land. In the spring, Arsene and I went camping, and that summer we spent time out fishing, and enjoying the peace and quiet of the open spaces.

When Johanna arrived, we increased our number of births, as we expanded our area to the other settlements in Kivalliq Region. I filled in at Chesterfield Inlet and twice at Whale Cove. It was a great experience for me and I was able to promote the Rankin Birthing Centre to the local women.

After Stuart, our youngest son, passed all his high school exams in Rankin, we decided that it was time to return to New Zealand to rescue our house from our other two sons and to be there for my elderly mother. It was a busy summer handing over the reins because of the expansion of the territory for the birthing centre. In October, 2000, we packed up once more and were on our way back to New Zealand, again leaving behind some good friends and family, knowing that we would be back in the not too distant future to start all over again in Rankin Inlet, Nunavut.

Working and living in Rankin three times over a period of thirty-two years, I witnessed many changes. It was a pleasure to see the establishment of the birthing centre, which had been demanded by the Inuit women, and to have played a part in its successful operation.

Chris Siksik trained at the Auckland School of Nursing from 1962 to 1966. She obtained her General Training and Midwifery qualifications in 1972.

SELDOM A DULL MOMENT

Audrey Woodget RSCN, SRN, PHN

I was working in the Yellowknife Health Unit in 1971, when we heard that a new nurse would be joining us. Her name was Jan Stirling, and her husband, a Major in the army, was being transferred to Yellowknife from Ottawa. We hoped that the Major's wife wouldn't be too snooty, and that she would have a good sense of humor. When Jan arrived, I was delegated to take her around and show her the areas we home-visited.

Because there was an outbreak of hepatitis A, we needed to do gamma globulin immunizations. Jan and I went down to a house in Old Town (the original Yellowknife) to get started. It had a porch, one living room and two bedrooms, with about fourteen people living there. We were on the porch and about to enter the house, when we noticed to our left a bench with two people on it having sex! The man looked up and said to Jan and me, "I won't be long. We have nearly finished. Then we will come in." We carried on giving the shots to the rest of the family, and soon they joined us inside. What a shock it was for Jan who had come straight from Ottawa. We have since had many laughs over this. There was no need to worry, as Jan lasted another twenty-five years there and is still going strong in Yellowknife.

* * *

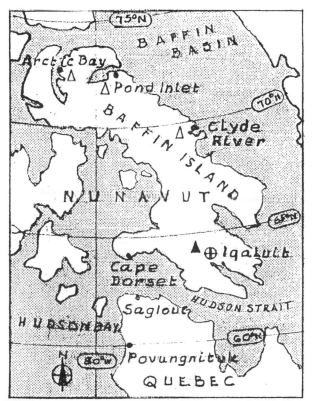

My husband, George, and I worked in Cape Dorset from 1966 to1969. During that time, we lived with our three-year-old daughter, Karen, in an apartment attached to the nursing station. We were the only two nurses for a population of around 700.

Since there was only one plane a month, it was difficult to send anyone out to Iqaluit, especially the prenatals. As a result, the women usually delivered at the nursing station or at home with the help of the mid-wife.

It had been a busy night, as we had already delivered three babies, and George and I were dead tired. We lay down on the bed with the newborn babies beside us so the moms could get some rest. We were awakened by our interpreter who told us that her mother was ready to deliver. This was her thirteenth baby. We ran down the hall that adjoined our room and saw that the birth was imminent. With one push, the woman delivered the baby and the placenta in a few minutes flat.

Unbeknownst to us, Karen's little head had come up at the end of the bed and she exclaimed, "Mummy, little baby and everything!" She cannot remember any of this, for which I believe she is truly thankful.

* * *

In the early 1970s at the Yellowknife Health Centre, we were doing all the medivacs. I remember one occasion when we had a call from Rae Lakes to say there was a very sick man who needed to be evacuated. It was my turn, so off I went in a single-engine plane. There was space for one pilot, one extra seat, and room for a stretcher. I am not the greatest passenger in a small plane, especially when there is turbulence.

We arrived and picked up the patient who had TB and was vomiting blood. With him on the stretcher and me in the spare seat, we took off. It was still extremely turbulent and I was not feeling well. I looked around for a bag. The only one I could see was the one the patient had and obviously needed. Knowing there wasn't much time to lose, I grabbed his bag and used it. The patient then explained that he couldn't breathe very well and needed to sit up. I changed places with him. He sat up on my seat while I lay down on his stretcher. We shared the bag all the way to Yellowknife.

When we arrived at the hospital, a nurse said to me, "You look green!" No wonder! Surprisingly enough, I didn't get TB.

Audrey Woodget started her nursing career in October, 1950 at Queen Mary's Hospital for Children in Carlshalton, Surrey, England (a branch of Great Ormand Street Hospital). At the end of a four-year programme, she qualified as a Registered Sick Children's Nurse. She took a three-year General Nursing programme in the Kent and Canterbury Hospital and obtained her RN. She met her husband, George, who was also nursing at that time, on the tennis court of Kent and Canterbury, and they decided to come to Canada. In Sarnia, Ontario, Audrey enrolled in an intensive OB course with a midwife from Scotland. She and George were married in 1959, and in 1962, they moved to the Arctic. In 1971, she completed her Public Health Diploma at UBC in Vancouver. George and Audrey stayed in the Arctic until 1998, with no regrets and with many wonderful memories. They now live on Vancouver Island.

MY FIRST SOLO FLIGHT

Michael J. Hewitt RN, RPN, PHN

February is usually a brutally cold month in the Northwest Territories, and February, 1965, was no exception. For days on end, there were clear skies and daytime temperatures of minus 40 to 45° Celsius, and at night, it got extremely cold. It was on such a day that I received a telephone call from my friend and colleague, Dr. Roland Thibaudeau, who lived 70 miles away in Fort Rae. "Michel, comment ça va?" his cheery voice boomed in my ear.

"Ça va bien, Roland, et vous?" I replied, exhausting my command of the French language.

"Michel, tomorrow we must go to Snare Lake. Since three weeks I 'aven't been, and I must do a clinic there," he said. "So please arrange a charter and pick me up 'ere tomorrow Michel, oui?"

"Oui," I responded, remembering another French word. "What time would you like to be picked up?"

"As soon as daylight is 'ere, and be sure to bring vaccines. We must do immunization also."

"Will a Cessna 185 do for us?" I asked.

"Oui, Michel, I don't hexpect to need anything bigger." We exchanged a few more pleasantries before ending the conversation. I organized the aircraft charter, setting 9:30 a.m. as the tentative departure time from Yellowknife.

About 65 air miles northwest from Yellowknife, lies Fort Rae, a Dene community, which in 1965 comprised some 700 people. On Snare Lake, 100 miles north of Fort Rae, was a small community of 250 Dene who lived in log houses on the western shore. They lived off the land, hunting, trapping and fishing in the wilderness. Sir John Franklin had passed through this area on his exploration of 1820-22. He travelled the length of Snare Lake in April of 1820, guided by Chief Akaitcho. The lake is about 15 miles long, and between one and three miles wide. Because lake trout and other fish are easily caught in its clear, pristine water, the Dene consequently ate a diet rich in protein. I loved going to these places, for, having been raised in an English city, it opened up a whole new world to me. I was fascinated by the wilderness and by the rugged people who lived there.

At 9:30 the next morning, "Smokey" Hornby eased the aircraft into the frigid air (it was minus 50°) and we banked westward towards Fort Rae. Smokey had expressed some misgivings about the extreme cold, worried that he might have trouble re-starting the aircraft if we stayed anywhere for too long. When we arrived at Fort Rae, we landed on Marion Lake in front of the hospital. There to greet us were Dr. Thibaudeau and another friend of mine, Ed Callas. Ed was the Indian agent for the area and I frequently travelled with him to the outlying settlements in order to share the air charter costs. (On one memorable occasion, I travelled with him in a Bombardier from Fort Rae to Lac La Martre – at least that is where we *meant* to go. I stood with my head sticking out of the roof hatch of the Bombardier, wearing sunglasses to keep my eyes from freezing. I was supposed to find a safe route across a frozen lake. Ed said I looked like the famous German General Rommel, the Desert Fox. We didn't make it across the lake, but broke through thin ice near the shore. However, that is another story.)

It took only a few moments to load the good doctor and his gear on board, and off we set for Snare Lake. We flew over the pre-Cambrian shield, with its rolling, rocky landscape speckled with countless lakes – a humbling experience. The land stretches into eternity, with no sign of habitation or roads. Travelling on foot, as Franklin had done, must have been exhausting, especially in bug season. Far better to fly over it at 3000 feet in winter. Everything was covered in snow, and we could often see the tracks of the many caribou wintering in the area.

The community of Snare Lakes was so tiny it would have been easy to fly over without seeing it. The log homes were banked with snow, and the dogs were tied out in lines below

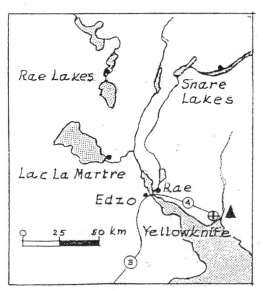

them. As usual, we landed on the frozen lake and taxied up to the shore. In no time, we had established our clinic in one of the homes. We spent the next several hours examining, treating and immunizing a large number of people. To my relief, no one required dental treatment. I was accustomed to extracting teeth, but had plenty to do without that distraction. Smokey Hornby would appear periodically and ask if we were ready to go. He was quite concerned as to whether his aircraft would start. Eventually, we finished, and hurried to the plane, boarded quickly, and waved goodbye to the hardy souls who came to see us leave.

Smokey turned the ignition key to start the aircraft. There was a low whine, then silence. He tried once or twice more, looked at us and said, "She won't turn over. We're going to have to start her with a rope." Turning to Dr. Thibaudeau, who had jumped into the front seat beside him, he asked, "Doc, do you mind coming with me and giving a haul on the rope?"

"Mais oui!" replied the doctor. Smokey looked at me questioningly.

"I think that's a big yes, Smokey," I answered, not anxious to get out of the aircraft.

They both climbed out; but before he left, Smokey showed me where the ignition key was. He told me to turn it when he had wound the rope around behind the prop, and was out of the way. The sequence of events was that I would switch on the ignition when Smokey shouted to me, and they would pull on the rope. They pulled on the rope – and fell backwards into the snow. The engine didn't start so we went through the whole routine again and again – at minus 45°C. Eventually the engine started, and Smokey leaped in and adjusted the throttle. I watched as he did this. He simply turned a knob located at the end of the throttle arm, and the engine slowed down a little. After that, it was just a matter of getting the half-frozen doctor on board, and away we flew.

The trip back to Fort Rae was uneventful. We made one pass over the community before we landed once more in front of the hospital. We were met by Ed Callas and the local RCMP corporal, Peter Pallister, who quickly unloaded the shivering doctor and his gear. They waited on the rocks near the shoreline in order to see us off.

Smokey turned the ignition key, and once again, the engine refused to ignite. With a deep sigh, he remarked, "Well Hewitt, here we go again." With that, he climbed down from the aircraft and to my relief, he was joined by Peter Pallister. I didn't fancy pulling on that rope and falling on my back into the snow. Which is exactly what Smokey and Pete Pallister did three or four times before the engine roared into life.

I noticed at once that it sounded louder than at Snare Lake. I waited to see if Smokey was coming to adjust things, when the aircraft began to move. I wasn't terribly concerned, since I thought I could quickly slow the engine down the way Smokey had done. But it didn't seem to have the same effect. I turned the knob with my left hand, only to detect a slight increase in noise. "Ah, wrong way," I thought. I began to turn it the other way, and I also had the bright idea of using the rudder pedals to bring the aircraft round in a circle. I actually completed one circle and once again had the pleasure of waving goodbye to Ed Callas and Dr. Thibaudeau. Then things began to go wrong....

Fort Rae sits on the shore of Marion Lake, a shallow body of water that empties into Great Slave Lake. The shoreline in the vicinity of the hospital is littered with small islands and rocky outcrops, which rise three or four feet above the water. The "runway," nothing more than a smooth stretch of frozen lake, neatly dissected these islands. It took no time at all to leave the narrow runway. I couldn't see where I was going and the speed of the aircraft was not sufficient to lift the tail off the ground. All I could see was the nose and propeller so I rotated the throttle knob and looked up at the sky wondering what would happen next. It never occurred to me to unbuckle my seat belt, stand up and take a look around. Before I knew what was happening, the plane hit the first rocky islet, bounced over the ground and gave me a good shaking. I twisted the knob a little harder and the plane immediately hit a larger island where I plowed through some scrub willow trees. At this moment, I glanced through the port (the pilot's) side window and saw two snow-covered apparitions vainly trying to catch up with the aircraft.

Clearly, this was a time for action on my part. I kicked the left rudder hard and turned the throttle knob. I noticed a definite reduction in engine noise, so I knew I was doing something right! Coming round in a circle enabled Smokey and Peter to "cut me off at the pass" and I knew I was saved when the pilot's door suddenly flew open. Snow-covered, with icicles hanging from his eyelashes, nose and beard, Smokey flung himself into the cockpit and switched off the ignition. "Now, why didn't I think of that?" I wondered. The engine died, then coughed into life as Smokey turned the key on and off in order to keep the engine running while he cleaned himself off and prepared to fly.

The door on my side swung open and Pete Pallister appeared, also covered in snow, but laughing despite the discomfort. He grabbed my arm and shouted above the noise of the engine, "General Rommel, I arrest you for flying without a license!"

Smokey never spoke on the way back to Yellowknife. Once we landed, however, he warned me, with a sad look on his face, "Don't ever charter my plane again. Never. Ever."

Michael Hewitt started his long career in the North in 1964. In 1966, he graduated as a public health nurse from Dalhousie University in Halifax, Nova Scotia. In 1981, he was appointed to the position of Assistant Deputy Minister for Justice and Public Services, responsible for all occupational health and safety for the Northwest Territories. He left the North in November, 1987 and is now doing consulting work in Nova Scotia.

WORK AND TRAVEL ACROSS CANADA'S NORTH

Rose Scrivens RN, CHN (NP)

In 1986, while finishing up the second leg of my internship for the Outpost Nursing course in Cape Dorset, NWT, I was scheduled to leave for Frobisher Bay, which is now called Iqaluit. It was not a bad evening in Cape Dorset. My friends, Heather and Dan, gathered my things together, and we all piled into the RCMP Suburban and headed off for the airport. When we arrived, we could hear the plane circling overhead. In fact, it circled several times before the airport announced that the pilot could not see to land. Back to the nursing station we went, hoping for better luck the next day. However, early the following morning, we got word that since the ceiling was still too low for them to attempt to land, they would not even take off for Cape Dorset. Fortunately for us, on the third day, it was "third time lucky." With baggage in hand, and friends to see us off and wish us a safe journey, we watched the plane make a safe landing. As we looked at each other, I'm sure we were each thinking the same thing, "Thank God the weather has cleared and it is safe to travel."

For twelve years, I worked in the North, ten in the Yukon and two in northern Ontario. I enjoyed my time there, especially the challenging work, which taught me patience, particularly when it came to travelling.

* * *

In 1987, I moved to Old Crow, Yukon, the most northern community in the Territory, accessible only by air. Early in my stay, I was presented with a challenge. During the holiday season, a twenty-one year old woman was celebrating both her birthday and Christmas. On Christmas Day, while drinking some home brew and taking large amounts of acetaminophen (I was not to learn of the latter until much later), she began to feel very ill. The family called me in on a home visit and I took an RCMP officer with me. After careful questioning, the family maintained that she had only drunk a little too much. So I gave her something to settle an upset stomach. No more was heard until the following evening, Boxing Day, just before midnight. I was in bed when the doorbell rang. Over the intercom, the person at the door simply said, "She won't wake." In a flash I was up and dressed and downstairs. I was confronted with the young lady I had treated the night before, together with her mother. The mother said, "She sleeps most of the time and when she sleeps, we can't wake her." Once more, I insisted on knowing what else she had taken, other than the alcohol. As before, they denied there was anything else.

I proceeded to treat the young lady using an NG (nasogastric) tube, catheter and two IVs. I consulted with the doctor-on-call in Inuvik who felt, as I did, that she had most probably

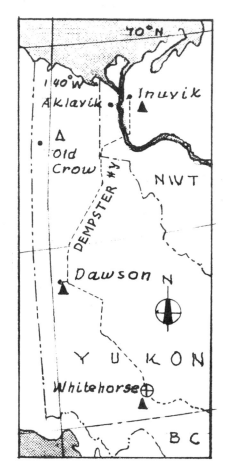

taken acetaminophen, but with the family not admitting it, we could not treat her appropriately. The next step was to get her out to a hospital. The problem was that the temperature was minus 50° and the planes would not fly below minus 40. As a consequence, with little or no sleep and in constant contact with the doctors in Inuvik, I had this young woman in a coma for the best part of three days.

What made matters worse was the fact that Old Crow was a one-nurse station, which meant I was the only one there. We had an exceptional support staff. However, due to the holidays, they were off work. Up to that point, I had only been treating emergencies and, thank heavens, it had not been too busy. I tried to snatch some sleep on a chair in the patient's room. Fortunately, we had excellent RCMP in the community, and whenever I needed something, I'd give them a call. They would stay with the patient, and I would be able to leave her long enough to get a bite to eat.

It was the third day before the weather finally broke and the plane arrived with a doctor and a nurse on board. It took off immediately, flying the woman to a hospital in Edmonton. Two days later, a call came in from a doctor there informing me that the patient was in a hepatic coma and that she had a high acetaminophen level. She was indeed lucky to be alive, but too much time had elapsed to treat her condition effectively. The doctor noted that the patient was flashing in and out of the coma and insisted that we find out what she had taken and how much.

An RCMP officer and I returned to the house in another attempt to find out exactly what the patient had taken. Again we were met with denials that anything other than alcohol was involved. As we walked back to the RCMP station, one of the patient's brothers came up behind us on his bicycle. Pulling a bottle out of his pocket, he asked, "Would this do anything, as we were taking these to get a high?" It was an acetaminophen bottle that held 500 tablets and now there were just a few left. Although they had eventually acknowledged what had happened, it was too late. It almost cost her her life. Several weeks later, she came out of the coma with only 10% of her liver functioning. She was able to come home, with the warning that if she drank or if she took acetaminophen again she could die.

* * *

On another night in Old Crow, there was a call from the RCMP about 3 a.m., telling us they were bringing in a lad who had put his arm through a store window. There were several large gashes in his arm, which took 40 stitches to close. After I had taken care of that, I cleaned up and returned to bed around 6 a.m., hoping for a little sleep. At 7 a.m., the doorbell rang. It was the janitor on the intercom informing us that someone who couldn't breathe very well was sitting on the front steps. So I got out of bed again and went down to talk to the young man. He said he had been stabbed in the chest with a pitchfork, and he was reluctant to tell me who had done it. Since I knew he could not stand long enough on his own for me to take an x-ray, I told him the RCMP would have to be called in and they would certainly need to know. He then admitted who it was. When I called the RCMP for assistance, I also asked them, "By the way, do you still have that gent whose arm I just stitched up in the cells?"

"No, we've just let him out," they answered.

"Well, you had better get somebody to round him up again. I have a patient here that I'm about to x-ray, with your help, who claims our boy just stabbed him in the chest with a pitchfork." My only experience with pitchforks had been with making hay. I knew they didn't make hay in Old Crow, nor did I think they had pitchforks here.

After the x-ray had been taken and developed, I wasn't quite sure what I was seeing. I suspected we were dealing with a collapsed lung, but hadn't seen an x-ray of one before. When I called the doctor and described it to him, he agreed that it was a collapsed lung. Arrangements would be made right away to fly a doctor and a nurse over, as the patient would need a chest tube put in before he could fly. When the plane arrived and the doctor took a good look at the x-ray and the injured man, he said the wound had come dangerously close to the heart. With the patient stable and the tube in place, they left for Inuvik. Soon after, I had a call from the doctor to say the fellow was indeed lucky, as the wound was within one centimetre of his heart. A week later, the lad was able to return home.

* * *

When I think of Old Crow, it isn't only my nursing experiences that come to mind. The only means of transportation was snowmobile in winter and three-wheeler in summer. If you were invited out to supper, you got on one of these vehicles, holding on to your lemon pie or whatever you were contributing to the meal – and away you went.

It is a fact of life for someone working in the North, that when you are far from home and have a craving for something good to eat, you will do just about anything to get it. For instance, a group of us in Old Crow decided that we needed a lobster supper (not too surprising, since I am from Nova Scotia) and we figured out how to get lobsters up to Old Crow with a minimum of time delay. We had heard that one of the RCMP was going to Whitehorse on a course and would be returning on the police plane. Taking advantage of this opportunity, I made the necessary arrangements to have the lobsters shipped up to Whitehorse in time to meet the returning police plane. The RCMP picked them up and continued on to Old Crow. I'll never forget how we all gathered outside and enjoyed our feed of boiled lobster.

* * *

In December of 1996, I was working in Lansdowne House in northern Ontario. A relief nurse had just come in that week, and at lunchtime, the same day the doctor had flown in to do her two-day clinic. Meanwhile, I was nursing the worst cold you could imagine. We had discussed going home on time that night, at least by 5 o'clock, so that I could get some rest. The doctor had even promised to cook supper for me. However, at 4 o'clock, a chap arrived at the station telling us there was a man out on the winter road who had been shot. He himself had travelled for an hour by Ski-Doo to inform us, but he didn't know how long the other man had travelled to tell him. It was minus 40°C and the road was not yet open, so a truck could only get so far and the rest of the way would have to be covered by snowmobile. When he suggested a nurse would be needed at the site, the relief nurse insisted on going, as I was too sick. I told her to make sure she was dressed warmly because it was minus 40, with a wind chill to consider. We were also aware that, due to the cold, one would be unable to use oxygen or IVs.

Off went the nurse on the snowmobile with the first responder. We had no idea how far out they were or how long they would be, what condition the patient might be in, or if he even was still alive. All we could do was get ready for the worst. I called Sioux Lookout Zone Hospital to prepare them for the possibility that we would need a plane. We started by filling up our incubator with IV solution to warm it up, and we organized what we thought might be needed. After that, it was just a waiting game until we heard something definite on the person's condition.

Of course, all evening there were lots of rumours flying around; but there was nothing concrete until about ten-thirty. A man came ahead of the others (who were with the injured person) to warn us that they were on their way and would be there in another 15 minutes or so. He told us that the patient was alive and was being pulled on a sled behind a snowmobile. I called Sioux Lookout immediately to advise them that a plane was required for medivac and I requested that they send blood.

When the patient arrived at the nursing station, we got most of the story. Apparently, he had been working on the winter road, when he had stopped to check something on his Ski-Doo. Two young lads from the neighbouring community were out moose hunting and had seen him bent over the snowmobile. They thought he was a moose and had fired nine shots at him. One had hit him in the chest and another had seriously damaged his left hand. Along with the victim, we had the young nurse with frostbite to both hands and face, as she had tried her best to stop the bleeding by wrapping a bandage around the victim's injured hand. Several of the first responders were also suffering from frostbite to their faces. The young fellows who had done the shooting were both severely shaken up.

The doctor and I started working on the chap who had been shot. The people from the community helped out by recording and being a tremendous support to the victim, constantly talking to him and encouraging him. It was to take us all night. The whole time, the patient was conscious and was talking to someone. His chest had entrance wounds, but no exit wounds. First we had to get two chest tubes in, a job the doctor and I shared. Because we didn't keep such tubes in the station, I improvised with clear IV connecting tubing. Somewhere I had learned that this tubing could be used for many different things and in this emergency, it worked well. The hand that was badly wounded was wrapped in wet dressings. The community support was more than overwhelming, in spite of the problems due to the cold weather, lower body temperatures and lack of warm blankets in a small nursing station.

It was none too soon when the plane with paramedics aboard arrived from Sioux. The pilot informed us that, with a temperature of minus 40°C and wind chill of minus 86, it was easy to get frostbite. We continued our efforts to stabilize the patient. We gave him four units of the blood brought in by the paramedics and more IV lines, and constantly monitored his vital signs. However, it wasn't until nearly 6 a.m. that he was stable enough to be flown out. A second plane was required to medivac the young nurse whose frostbite was severe and the two lads who were in dire need of mental health counselling.

* * *

By now, it was almost noon. We had not only missed last night's supper, a night's sleep and breakfast but this was another day and, because the doctor was only in town once every four to six weeks, we had to try to carry on as usual. It was very difficult, as we were constantly thinking about the people we had treated the previous night, especially someone injured that severely. Of special concern to us was the fact that a co-worker needed to be medivac'd.

At lunchtime, we got word back on our first patient. The bullet, which had entered the chest through his right lung, had bounced off his ribs, gone down through his liver and through his bowel. A very lucky man. He had a rough road ahead, requiring chest and abdominal surgery, plus plastic surgery to his hand. Six months later, he returned to the community almost totally recovered. He had lost partial use of his left hand but he considered himself fortunate to be alive.

* * *

Now back in Nova Scotia, I often think of these northern experiences. My time in the North was very special to me. I met many wonderful people and I thrived on the challenge of the work.

Rose Scrivens graduated from St. Martha's School of Nursing in Antigonish in 1978. She worked at Victoria General Hospital in Halifax until August 1983, when she moved to the Yukon for *a year*. She worked at several nursing stations, until she returned to Nova Scotia. In July, 1985, she completed the Outpost Community Health Program at Dalhousie in Halifax. During her internship, Rose worked in Sioux Lookout, Iqaluit and Cape Dorset prior to graduating in December, 1986. On her return to the Yukon, she was nurse-in-charge in Old Crow and in Carmacks until she left the Yukon in December, 1989. She later worked in Lansdowne House in Northern Ontario. Rose is currently a long-term care placement coordinator in Kentville, Nova Scotia.

RAPID DELIVERY AT THE "MIDNIGHT MOTEL"

Kate Hamilton RN, SCM

My most memorable nursing experience in northern Canada happened when I worked at the Grenville Mission in northern Newfoundland. I had been there for three weeks working in the obstetrics ward as a staff nurse. We were expected to do medivacs, which I had never had any experience in.

A call came on my day off, asking if I would pick up a patient arriving by ferry across the Strait of Belle Isle from Blanc Sablon. There was a nurse with the patient, but it was felt there should also be a midwife. I collected all the emergency equipment, which consisted of a bottle of oxygen in a trolley, a couple of bags with instruments and the maternity pack. Off I went with the driver in a station wagon, which served as an ambulance.

When the ferry arrived at St. Barbe, the patient was unloaded into the back of the station wagon. The nurse reported that the mother was not in labour. After introductions, we headed for the hospital in St. Anthony, which was about a sixty-mile drive away. This patient was being sent over to the main hospital for a c-section, as she was Rh negative with antibodies. This was her sixteenth pregnancy.

The roads were muddy and slippery. From her facial expression and the little noises she made, I suspected that this woman was in labour. I had no sooner expressed my thoughts to the nurse than the station wagon skidded off the road and sailed over a 10-15 foot embankment. We landed nose first, at a 75-degree angle. I could hear hissing, and quickly realized that the oxygen cylinder had been wrenched open. I threw it out of the car in case it exploded. The patient, a large woman, was still on the stretcher, but at an awkward angle. I managed to open the door and squeeze into the back. I searched through my bag and found a pair of gloves to examine her. To my horror, she was almost fully dilated. Decisions had to be made quickly.

The driver and the other nurse climbed up the embankment to flag down a vehicle. Meanwhile, I explained to my patient that she was

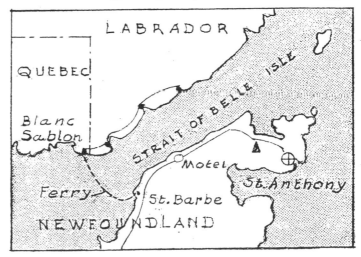

almost ready to deliver her baby. I requested that she please not push. The mother was calm and quiet, and as far as I could see, uninjured except for a swelling face. The other two were successful in getting a truck to stop, and two old men helped us get the stretcher out of the car and up the bank. The truck was open at the back and full of oil drums but we all managed to fit, with the stretcher balancing on top of the oil drums.

The nurse remembered that there was a motel close by, and the old men confirmed that it was about thirteen miles away. (Thinking that they had said three miles, I figured we would probably make it.) My patient was having contractions, but was in no distress. We stopped at a camp back in the bush so that the driver could call the hospital and have the obstetrician meet us at the motel.

When we arrived at the motel, we quickly asked for a room and explained the situation to the startled host. We were given a tiny room and we laid the stretcher on the bed. By this time, the patient was ready to deliver. Again, I pleaded with her not to push. As she had had so many pregnancies and it was likely she would hemorrhage, I set up an intravenous. I found the cord clamp and scissors. (The bag was packed for every obstetrical emergency and it was difficult to locate the simple things.) Finally, I was ready and delivered the baby with no trouble.

The obstetrician arrived in time to assist the nurse with the baby who needed help to start breathing and who became jaundiced before our eyes. I delivered the placenta and tidied up. We transferred the patient and baby to a "real" ambulance, which resembled the jeep-type used in M*A*S*H. The area that held the stretcher was narrow and I was terrified the patient would fall off. I spent thirty uncomfortable minutes holding her on the stretcher.

We eventually arrived at the hospital with a much relieved patient, a jaundiced baby and two exhausted nurses who were now able to pay attention to their own broken bones!

Kate Hamilton came to Canada from Scotland and worked with the Grenfell Mission in northern Newfoundland and Labrador. After moving to the Northwest Territories in 1972, she nursed in several communities and is presently a public health nurse in the Yellowknife Health Centre.

TADOULE LAKE, NORTHERN MANITOBA

Carolyn Conrad (Shorten) Anderson RN

Consider this: you now work for the Medical Services Branch of Health Canada and have been assigned a position in one of the many nursing stations in Manitoba. The working environment requires a whole different mindset, and after 20 years of hospital nursing experience, it is often very hard for you to adjust. Flexibility is a great asset.

You are to be nurse-in-charge at the nursing station in Tadoule Lake and are given a two-day orientation to all the paperwork. You now work for the government; hence all the red tape! It is interesting how you can never find the correct form when you need it, or how the form you would assume comes under a specific heading, doesn't. Even though each station is supposed to have at least two nurses at all times, you find that you are on your own. Things aren't always what they seem. You come to realize that, for some reason, you haven't asked the right questions. Two rules of the North: "never assume," and "hurry up and wait."

You learn that the communities each have their own inherent culture. You learn that, in times of crisis, everyone comes to help. A ten-year-old boy may surprise you when he asks, "Can I help?" It's called "the moccasin telegraph," and it works better than a telephone, you are told.

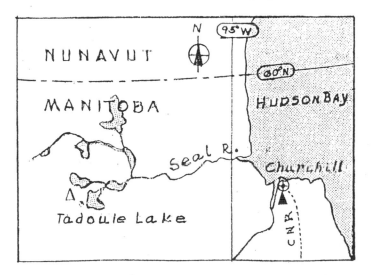

At the time of your employment in Tadoule Lake, you find out that it is one of the very few communities that have indoor washroom facilities. However, the planes that fly into these communities are not equipped with washrooms. Your mother had flown in to visit you while you were at another nursing station and she discovered it personally.

It is a little unnerving when you are in a four-seater plane and the pilot asks you if anything looks familiar. At that point, it is really convenient to be able to distinguish a winter road, for in the snow, you can at least see where to go. The weather is beautiful as the plane lands at Tadoule. You are the only passenger. Except for a lone vehicle, the airport is vacant. The pilot checks out both the vehicle and the driver. Upon his return to the plane, he informs you that you have a ride to the nursing station. Should you be worried?

On arriving at the station, you call out, "Is anyone home?" and a response of, "Oh, you're here!" comes from far away. You think this is strange, as there is only one flight a day. When asked how you travelled from the airport, you describe the vehicle and are told you have made a grand arrival with the alleged local drug dealer. Just great! The nurse you are replacing is packing. She catches up on the paperwork before she leaves the following day. You notice that you can't see the top of the office desk because there is so much paper on it. You are told by the nurse not to worry about it because it's the weekend. And besides, she'll return in a few months. The tour of the nursing station is carried out in short order and pertinent information is written down. There is a terrible odour of mould, and you are told it is from under the station. On departing, the outgoing nurse tells you that the whole community has been warned not to give you a hard time. Of course, you should have asked what a "hard time" meant. Just a little something you should know for future reference.

* * *

It may be hard to imagine, but that was my introduction to Tadoule Lake. Over that first weekend, I saw 31 clients. Not bad for a nursing station that wasn't supposed to be busy! On Monday, when I called the zone office requesting some directions on another matter, I was asked, "What are you doing?" (That is like saying to someone you call on the phone, "Oh, you are home.") "It's not supposed to be busy." Famous last words.

That was the day I decided that I had to take some control over the disorder and untidiness of the working area. I set myself a schedule, determined to go into the clinic from 6:30 to 8:30 in the morning and dedicate this time to paperwork, cleaning, and ordering. Zone soon notified me that these duties should be carried out between 8:30 and 5:00. I brought it to their attention that the time sheets were still here from other nurses, dating back three months. That particular directive alone was enough to make me wonder what toes I may already have stepped on, unknowingly.

As an afterthought, when the permanent nurse had left, I was informed that the full-time receptionist was on maternity leave. Within six days, I medivac'd the community health representative, an invaluable person who works with the nurse and the community. Things started to deteriorate when the fax machine didn't work for the following seven days. If that weren't enough, the power often went out, and the back-up generator wouldn't switch on. The hose for water went into the lake, and for approximately a third of my time in Tadoule, we had no running water because of blockages in the hose at the lake end. In addition, the Chief and

Council, for whatever reason, had some concerns over the running of the local store, and it was closed without notice.

Despite these disruptions, the daily routine went on. Many women elders started coming to the clinic and in most cases, they needed follow-up when the doctor flew in once a week. It gave me a sense of accomplishment to see that these women had a thorough clinical exam.

I had a nagging feeling that the clinic would be short of certain drugs. Not knowing the community, and with the CHR away on sick leave, I wondered if the supplies would be adequate. I discovered that there was only one Ventalin puffer (for asthma) and five Glucophage tabs (for diabetes). After examining the Chronic List, kept in every community for long-term follow-ups, I found I had to borrow supplies from other stations, which isn't recommended as that cost comes out of their operating budget. Just how was I to know what was going to be needed?

By the second week of September, the snow had already started coming down, followed by a several days of rain. This created an interesting transportation problem as one area got washed out. Boat transportation became necessary to access the nursing station from part of the town. One afternoon, a client arrived at the station by canoe and requested that a new cast be applied. When asked what happened to the old one, he answered, "I soaked it off coming in the boat." After the consultation, the client didn't get a cast.

* * *

During my stay in Tadoule, there was to be a celebration and a feast in the beautiful new school built by the community. Wanting to help, I offered my services, and my job became that of cook. Four caribou hindquarters needed to be prepared. The lady who gave me the meat was apologetic for the men's cleaning technique, but soaking the hindquarters in my bathtub solved the problem. Between the nursing station and the residence, all four could be cooked at the same time, as there were four stoves. They were done to perfection, I was told. My zone nursing officer, who was flying in for the celebration, had her secretary call to ask if there was anything I needed. I replied, "Yes, I'd like some diet Coke and milk."

"Why don't you buy them at the store?" was the response. An explanation ensued. (Coke was $9.25 a litre – *when* the store was open.)

When the zone nursing officer arrived, she said to me, "You should come to the feast." As it turned out, the clinic had clients off and on all afternoon, so I didn't get to go. However, there had been a miscalculation, which meant that there was no accommodation for the rock band that had flown in to play for the event. Hence I was to hear, "You wouldn't mind keeping the band at the residence, would you?" They (all six members) stayed three nights!

* * *

While I was in Tadoule, the dentist made his usual visit, and it was our luck that he was an avid fisherman. We certainly enjoyed the benefits, and in return, I baked muffins with berries provided by members of the community. The previous permanent nurse seemed to have had an open-door policy, and it was nice to have local people drop in, either as a couple or by themselves, to enjoy some baked goods.

The Dene of Tadoule had a lovely community hall where the men played traditional hand games each night and the women played cards. The drums the men played always seemed to mesmerize. Their sound carried into the evening air and offered a sense of peace with the dancing of the northern lights. As my time was drawing to a close, I realized that the people of Tadoule Lake hadn't given me "a hard time." They were respectful and didn't abuse the health care system. Some may have implied otherwise, but respect for people and their culture goes both ways.

* * *

The snow was now permanently on the ground and I was heading to Brochet, another station in northern Manitoba, where I was supposed to have been from the first week in July. It was closer to October and my overtime sheets showed my hours as 913.

Carolyn Anderson graduated from the Victoria General Hospital School of Nursing in March, 1972. She worked for twenty years in Nova Scotia hospitals before heading north to Iqaluit and the Baffin Regional Health Board. She joined the Medical Services Branch of Health Canada in Manitoba and nursed in northern communities. She completed the Northern Clinical Program at McMaster University in Hamilton, Ontario. Unfortunately, her working career in the northern nursing stations was cut short by illness. She has three grown children and lives with her husband, Oscar, in South Indian Lake.

TWELVE DAYS IN LANSDOWNE HOUSE

Kenneth Penrose BA (Honours)

My ultimate destination was Lansdowne House, an Ojibwa community in the far north of Ontario. I had completed the first two-hour leg of my journey from Toronto to Thunder Bay via Air Canada. My connecting flight with Bearskin Airlines was due in at any moment. Ten of us, each with our limited baggage, watched as the small ten-seater aircraft landed and taxied our way. It stopped close to a gas storage tank, and the young pilot, and his even younger female co-pilot, disembarked. The co-pilot refuelled the plane much the same as you would a car at a gas station. She removed the filler cap from the plane's wing and plugged in the hose. Having refuelled, they stored our baggage and allowed us to board.

The small plane was as different as you could imagine from the familiar commercial airliner most of us are used to. It was strictly functional transportation, with two rows of five seats, no toilets and no flight attendants. The seats were separated from the pilot and co-pilot by a meagre strip of drab curtain that wasn't drawn. This allowed the two of us in the front seats a fairly good view of where we were going. The crew quarters seemed equally as Spartan as those of the passengers, perhaps more so.

Having determined that all seats were occupied, the crew settled into their seats. Within a few moments, the engine started and we taxied toward our allotted runway. Once airborne, we were soon beyond the city limits of Thunder Bay, flying over the rugged landscape of northern Ontario. Our first port of call was Geraldton, about 60 miles north of Lake Superior and east of Lake Nipigon. We taxied toward the tiny airport and stopped by a gas storage tank. We left the plane and waited in the terminal for about fifteen minutes. When we re-boarded, we discovered that we had lost two of our passengers. They were probably engineers or technicians who worked on one of the many projects in this part of Ontario. The remaining passengers were six Ojibwa (three men, two young women and a small boy), an engineer and myself.

We left Geraldton and headed north for Fort Hope, the last touchdown before our final destination at Lansdowne House. The terrain had changed. All signs of habitation were gone, only trees, sparse scrub, lakes, and thin streams linking them together. No green was in sight, and although it was the 24th of May, patches of ice hugged the shoreline of the myriad lakes.

After an hour of flying, we began to lose height as we approached Fort Hope. Below us, we could see the Albany River. Stretching west to east from Lake St Joseph, it meanders 610 miles before emptying into James Bay, at historic Fort Albany, a vital part of Canada's heritage. It was the highway of the fur traders and the voyageurs. What I saw was unchanged since the voyageurs passed this way centuries ago. The only changes then, as today, were those made by the seasons.

When we landed at Fort Hope, we left the plane while the ritual of refuelling took place. We stretched our legs, made use of the facilities, and went back on board. We were now seven, the six Ojibwa and I. When we reached flying altitude for the last leg of our journey, there were smiles and nods from my co-passengers. As I smiled back, one of the young women asked, "Where you from?"

"I'm from Toronto," I replied.

There were more smiles and nods as she inquired, "Where you go?"

"I'm going to Lansdowne House," I answered.

Then came the critical question. "You go stay with Nurse Rose? You Nurse Rose uncle?"

"Yes. I'm Nurse Rose's uncle."

It was clear that the community was expecting me, and judging from the smiles and nods accompanying my answers, it was evident that Nurse Rose was held in high regard. During the next twelve days, I would meet most of the adults and the children in this small and isolated community.

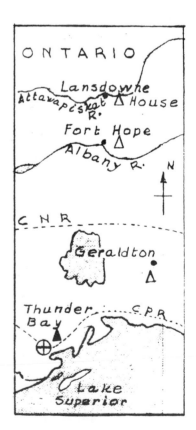

* * *

We began our descent. The landing strip at Lansdowne House was a clearing in the forest, a few acres of mud rolled flat, and the airport was a small frame building which looked like a garden shed. There were a couple of battered pickup trucks and a four-wheel drive parked at the bottom of the wooden steps leading up to the "terminal." As the plane taxied toward the inevitable gas tank, my fellow passengers gathered their belongings and chattered excitedly. It was clear that they were coming home. When the plane came to a halt, the co-pilot opened the door and lowered the steps. As we assembled at the bottom and waited for our bags, the drivers of the pickup trucks came over and greeted their family members. The driver of the four-wheel approached me. "Mr. Ken? I am Hilda Moonias. Nurse Rose ask me to come and get you as she is busy in the hospital. I work with Nurse Rose."

I collected my single suitcase, dumped it into the back of the transport, and climbed aboard. Hilda started up and we pulled away amid waves and shouts from my fellow passengers and their family members. Hilda and I waved back as we headed down a rutted track that, I suspect a few weeks previously, had been a sea of mud. We soon came to the end of the track and pulled on to a wider track. Hilda turned left. I learned later that this was the one and only road, eight kilometres long, which linked the old community of Lansdowne House with the newer settlement.

The road surface, like that of the airport landing strip, was packed mud and showed all the evidence of damage caused by the winter frost. Driving on these muddy, frost-heaved roads was hazardous. While Hilda wrestled the four-wheel from one side of the road to the other and attempted to avoid the deep potholes, I hung on and braced myself, wondering what I had let myself in for. There was no sign of habitation. At intervals along the roadside, there would be derelict cars, with missing parts. They had been abandoned where they had broken down or run out of gas. Occasionally, a large cloud of dust moved toward us. When it came closer, a vehicle would emerge, weaving from side to side of the road as we did. Hilda would slow down, and as we passed, there would be hand waving and shouts of greeting. Hilda would turn to me and smile, "That was so and so." I felt I would like to know all of these people who seemed so friendly and happy.

After about twenty minutes of driving, we finally arrived at habitation. A large single-storey building appeared on our right. A long wheelchair ramp leading up to the entrance marked it as the nursing station. Beyond the station, the rest of the town was laid out in two orderly rows of neat, single-story, white frame homes. The road ended at a huge pile of granite boulders, and the pine trees began again. Through them, I could see the late afternoon sun glinting on a large body of water.

This community of Lansdowne House was relatively new. Early in 1990 the band elders made the decision to relocate from the old Lansdowne House, eight kilometres back on the road we had just travelled. It consisted of 56 white frame dwelling houses on three roads, three long low schoolhouses, a large community hall, the nursing station, a generating station and a nurses' residence. There was apartment accommodation for a visiting doctor, dentist, or various therapists who would fly in on a regular basis.

It was now the late 1990s and not all of the 350 people of Lansdowne House had moved to the new location. Almost half of the families remained at the old site. There was one general store, which provided both communities with food and the necessities of living: clothing, hardware, guns, ammunition, fishing gear and toys. It also served as the post office and more importantly, as a meeting place.

The overwhelming feeling of culture shock I had experienced during the drive from the airport was beginning to subside as Hilda took me into the nursing station and left me in the capable hands of my niece, Rose Scrivens, the nurse-in-charge. For years, Rose, a veteran of almost twenty years of outpost nursing, had encouraged me to visit one of her stations. Now I was about to see first hand what happens in an isolated community where the responsibility for any medical problem lies with the outpost nurse. It could be just a runny nose or the whole gamut of medical situations: childbirth, broken bones, gunshot or knife wounds, substance abuse among the young, or any of the ailments that fill doctors' offices and emergency clinics in our urban and suburban environments. Most often, the nurse is the only non-native in the community. If she is lucky, a nursing assistant will be assigned to her, or perhaps she will get a young university-nursing student who is working on her elective. The nearest doctor is a phone call away, and provided the weather is favourable and the airfield is usable, he or she may fly in. The nurse is on call seven days a week, 24 hours a day.

* * *

Nick Moonias, Hilda's husband, arrived early the next morning to say he was taking me fishing. Nick had brought his young son, Kenny, a lad of about ten, who was all smiles and had boundless energy. We drove through the woods, until the rutted track led out to a small bay, which opened into a large lake. The water was calm and shimmered in the sunshine. In the far distance, I saw the edge of the ice. A few feet above the water's edge was a great-looking canoe about five and a half metres long, in excellent condition. Nick hauled an outboard motor out of the pickup truck, then rods and a tackle box. The three of us turned the canoe over onto its keel, and while Nick clamped the outboard onto the stern, Kenny and I put the tackle aboard. We slid it down into the water and Nick settled into the stern and started the outboard. Kenny and I got into the canoe and Nick gave the motor enough power to pull us off the shallow, sloping beach.

It wasn't long before we left the small bay behind and could see where the treeline met the shoreline. To our right, was a large expanse of ice and on our left, the uneven shoreline of jack pine and spruce, with fallen trees lying partly in the water. At one point, I heard a splash and saw a dark head swimming toward a large pile of logs and vegetation. I had my first glimpse of a beaver lodge. Soon the dark head became a fat beaver, as it clambered onto the lodge carrying something in its mouth. It began, unhurriedly, making what seemed to be repairs, then slid down the side and disappeared into the water. Although we were less than twenty feet away, we were totally ignored. Perhaps Nick, Kenny and the canoe were part of its environment, and for a brief moment, I like to think I was too.

When Nick killed the motor, we baited our hooks and began to cast. My knowledge of fishing was limited to the occasional fly-fishing for trout in Nova Scotia with Rose's father. Although I have had a fascination for water since I was a child and have sailed most of the world's oceans, I have never caught the fishing bug. It was, therefore, quite a surprise when within seconds of my baited hook hitting the water it registered a bite. The fish was clearly quite large because of the fight it put up. Nick shouted advice and with encouragement from Kenny, I worked at getting it close to the side of the boat so that Nick could net it. Nick managed to get the net under the fish and it fought, wriggled and flopped into the bottom of the boat.

The fish was a pike – about 20 inches long with a mouth full of vicious looking teeth. Nick had an Ojibwa name for it. I gripped the back of its head and began inexpertly to remove my hook. As the hook became free, the fish returned the favour by clamping its teeth on my thumb and drawing blood. For my two companions, this was highly amusing. Nick said, "You no put finger in fish's mouth. It like to bite." He then added, "You throw him back in water. We no eat him." With great care, I lifted my catch, dropped it over the side, and watched as it quickly disappeared, none the worse for its short captivity, I hoped.

Kenny was the next to get a bite and with more efficiency than I, he soon had his catch close enough so that his dad could net it. It was another pike, a little larger than mine and equally as active. Kenny, eyeing its double row of teeth, backed away and let his dad remove the hook and drop it back over the side. Nick restarted the outboard and we headed toward the ice. Slowly skirting the edge, he trolled a little with his line. It wasn't long before he had landed a healthy-looking trout. "Good," he said. 'This supper. Now we go in. I show you how to make it ready for eating."

We were soon back at the little bay and hauled the canoe high up on the beach. Nick carefully stored the outboard in the back of the truck, together with the tackle. As Kenny explored the shore, Nick laid the fish on an old tree stump and, with a few strokes of a sharp knife, took off the head and tail and reduced it to two nice plump fillets. Obviously, the old tree stump had a clearly defined purpose. It was equally evident that our fishing expedition was not sport, but a lesson on how a native community forages for food. The Ojibwa are hunter-gatherers.

At Lansdowne House, I had the pleasure of meeting Father Giles Gauvreau, the only other non-native member of the community. Father Giles, a member of the Oblates of Mary Immaculate, served the native people for 25 years in Ontario's isolated northern communities. His residence, together with an elegant white frame chapel, was on an island, accessible in the winter by snowmobile, and in the summer by canoe, or by a long rickety wooden walkway built on piles driven into the lakebed. Due to the pressure of the ice in winter, the walkway had to be repaired each spring, a job expertly handled by local band members.

Father Giles was a cheerful and hospitable man with a fund of interesting and amusing stories to tell. All visits began with a cup of coffee poured from a twelve-cup coffee maker. "Turning on the coffee maker is my first task in the morning," he told me, "and the last task at night is turning it off." He was an avid fisherman. Parked around the residence were signs of an active man: a snowmobile, a small powerboat and a canoe. Although we fished all one afternoon, swapped stories and laughed, we caught nothing. Thankfully, our supper did not depend on our catch. Since my visit, Fr. Giles regrettably passed away suddenly at Lansdowne House on January 6, 2000.

* * *

Each supper was a collective event, its timing dependent on how quickly the last medical emergency could be taken care of after 5 o'clock. Rose and I, Chantelle Dunlop (a nursing student from McMaster University doing her elective under the tutelage of Rose), and any visiting health care professional would eat together. The first couple of days I was there, a young visiting dentist not only took care of the dental needs of the community, but he also made a delicious apple pie. Everyone appreciated his contribution to the evening meal.

After supper Rose, Chantelle, and I walked around the village. The neat rows of houses were laid out like an urban subdivision. Most had piles of logs ready for the winter, and here and there was a line of washing. Some houses had a truck or a car parked outside, and a few had snowmobiles. What was most obvious was the total lack of landscaping. Nothing was planted and nothing grew: no grass, no shrubs, just bare scarred earth, a testament to the harsh climate, where in long winters, the temperatures often ranged to minus fifty.

* * *

The Ojibwa is a society trapped between two cultures. They are friendly and cheerful, and their children are like all children in any community: playful, inquisitive and active. Incidentally, many had been given names of Hollywood film stars, taken either from magazines or television. They hunt, fish and gather fuel for winter, skills developed to combat the harsh environment. These skills are passed on to their young. However, they are becoming more dependent on provincial or federal governments. A variety of foods are imported to supplement their diet, such as: frozen foods, eggs, potatoes and bread as well as cookies, soft drinks and candies. At the general store, they also buy their survival tools: guns, ammunition, fishing gear, chainsaws, snowmobiles and vehicles.

Exposure to television, radio, magazines and print media inevitably raises comparisons between their way of life and what they see portrayed in the mass media. For the elders and seniors of the community, these comparisons are purely academic. They know who they are and are proud of their heritage. However, it is the young who have the greatest difficulty withstanding these comparisons. It surfaces in the suicide rates and statistics on substance abuse. There is an argument to make for adding the figures for substance abuse to the figures on suicides, for it is my belief that both are cries for help. The saddest invasion of their culture is the absolute dependence they have on the outpost nurse and the nursing station for the health of their community.

I was sad to leave Lansdowne House. I was exposed to a culture so different from anything I had known. I made friends not only with the adults, but also with the children. It is the young people who are the future of these remote communities. I sincerely hope that the impact of any changes on these children will not diminish their proud heritage and the knowledge of who they are.

At the age of seventeen, *Ken Penrose* followed his childhood dream. He joined the British Merchant Marine and sailed the oceans of the world. Not only was he able to see many countries but, more importantly, he had the opportunity to meet different people and experience various cultures. At the outbreak of WW II, he was transferred to the Royal Navy. For the next six years, he saw more of the world from a different perspective. In 1948, he and his wife decided to make a new life for themselves by emigrating to Canada – a country he maintains has been good to them. After thirty-one years of working for Bell Canada, he decided to follow another dream. With encouragement from his wife, he decided to retire at sixty and enrol full-time at university. In 1988, he graduated from Glendon College (York University) in Toronto with an honours degree in History and Political Science. Now, in his early eighties, he still continues to dream.

EARLY DAYS OF NURSING IN THE NWT

Barbara Bromley CM, BSc, RN

In the late 1950s, a Graduate Nurse Association with hospital and married nurses was formed in the community of Yellowknife. Our group approached the two doctors to see if we could start immunization clinics. This would relieve the congestion of injured miners, pregnant women and moms with new babies in their small waiting room. The doctors were delighted with the suggestion. We soon held biweekly baby and immunization clinics in the nurses' recreation room at the Red Cross Hospital.

The hospital gave us needles and syringes, and lent us a small sterilizer. The doctors provided the vaccines, and Medical Services in Ottawa provided pamphlets, food guides, and mother and child books. The town of Yellowknife gave us $100 to get record cards for clients and to print record forms for our clinic. Betty Prince and I were both public health nurses, and along with other nurses from the group, we continued with the clinic and held polio vaccination clinics several times over the years.

In 1963, Medical Services in Ottawa opened a public health clinic in Yellowknife with Joe Atkinson and Anne Pask. Catherine Keith, the regional nursing officer for the Mackenzie Zone, NWT, was a dedicated nurse who was anxious to see nursing standards improve throughout the North. She encouraged me to join the staff in Yellowknife that winter.

* * *

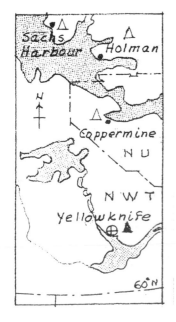

What was supposed to be my first medivac occurred late one night in the winter, when a call came from Holman Island to say that an Inuk was very ill. The lay dispenser, a Roman Catholic priest, suggested it might be a heart attack. The doctor on call decided that I should go and assess the client. There was a Hercules plane carrying drums of fuel leaving for Holman Island immediately. I scurried around getting my sleeping bag and nurse's bag together, while my husband made me a sandwich and a thermos of coffee. It was one a.m. when I left.

It was a cold night, even colder at Holman Island. The flight was uneventful and uncomfortable. I sat on the floor in the back of this huge plane, with 40 or so 45-gallon drums of fuel behind me. At Holman Island, we landed on an ice strip. The priest, who was waiting for us, took me up the hill to see the patient. I was surprised to find a real igloo, the first I had ever seen. We crawled through the short passageway, and stood up in a very warm, round room, dimly lit with a seal oil lamp. A snow bench went around the inside, most of it covered with caribou hides. In one corner, was the old Inuk, with his daughter sitting beside him. The priest and the daughter talked back and forth in Inuktitut, as I examined the patient. I listened to his chest and heart, and took his blood pressure, which was normal. He had a slight cough, but no temperature. His lips were dry and cracked, and he was very agitated.

The conversation continued with the father, the daughter and the priest, and I gathered that the old man did not want to leave his home and his daughter. The priest informed me that the man's wife had been sent out with TB, and that they did not know where she had gone, or even if she were still alive. I sensed that the daughter did not want her father to leave. She was afraid that he, too, might not come back.

I decided not to evacuate the patient, and suggested to the priest that he tell the daughter to give her father lots of fluids, and to keep him warm. The priest gave her cough syrup from his dispensary. I left the igloo and returned to the plane with some misgivings. I knew the priest was not pleased with my decision not to evacuate, and as I climbed aboard, I wondered if my supervisor would feel the same.

The flight back to Yellowknife was even worse. I sat with a cargo of empty 45-gallon drums, which made loud, popping noises as we flew. I arrived home at six a.m. and fell into bed exhausted, partly because I was uneasy about my decision to leave the patient at home.

When I went to work in the afternoon, I was greeted by Miss Pask who asked, "Well, Barb, how was your first medivac?" I told her the story, and to my relief, she agreed that I had done the right thing. We were able to trace the Inuk's wife to Edmonton, where she was being treated for TB. We heard later that this same man (whom I was to bring out to hospital) had improved. He had recovered and was out on the land again.

This experience made me aware of the closeness of the Inuit family. I had a sense of how these people must feel with the changes brought on by the arrival of the white man. It was my first medivac – but as time went on, I did many more, and I did bring patients back with me.

Barbara Bromley worked intermittently as a nurse in Yellowknife from 1948 to 1963. From 1965 to 1967, she was nurse-in-charge at the Yellowknife Public Health Centre. When she lost her husband, she took over his hardware business until 1975. Later, she became coordinator of the Home Care Program at Stanton Yellowknife Hospital and held that position until 1982. Barbara Bromley has received many awards for service including the Canada Volunteer Award in 1989 and The Order of Canada in 2000. The citation for the latter award reads:

> *She is the quintessential Volunteer. Active in her community, this registered nurse was the first in the city to speak out as a proponent for the elderly and is a founding member and director of the Yellowknife Association of Concerned Citizens for Seniors. Whether volunteering at the hospital or with the local Scouts, she is always generous with her time. Deeply committed to the city's residents, she has been a caregiver, activist, organizer and most importantly, a friend to many in the community.*

MY BEST CHRISTMAS EVER: POVUNGNITUK, 1975

J. Karen Scott, RN, BScN

I had been working in Sioux Lookout Zone in northern Ontario for fifteen months, during which time I had completed the course for nurse practitioners in Toronto. A call came from Miss Maria Skov, the regional nursing officer in Ottawa who asked if I would be available to relieve for a month in Povungnituk, in northern Quebec. First I had to look for Povungnituk on the map. I found it just above the 60th parallel on the Hudson Bay coast. Having never been to that part of the country, and having never worked in an Inuit village, the unknown presented a challenge for me. I packed my best Ports silk blouse as my contribution to Christmas fashion, along with a full supply of thermal underwear, and I was off.

It was in mid-December when I arrived at the Toronto Airport from Sioux, where I had been relieving in the public health office. There was time only for a quick Christmas drink with my father, sister and brother (my mother having died some years earlier), before I had to change terminals and travel on to Montreal.

On Monday morning, I reported to the federal medical and nursing officers for the Quebec region. Both officers were upset about what had transpired in Povungnituk (known to those who worked in the North as POV). Originally, there had been two federal nurses in the station. However, when a provincial doctor and nurse arrived from Montreal, they had apparently run the two federal nurses out of the station. The two nurses were now working in Saglouc, farther north from POV. I would later have two days with the doctor on his return from a vacation. I quickly understood why the federal nurses had left. (This was prior to the transfer of northern health services from Ottawa to the provinces, which made the situation tense.) My job was to reclaim the nursing station for the federal government, if only temporarily. I was given great latitude in how I was to accomplish this. Three days later, I was on my way to POV.

On the first day, we got as far as Val d'Or where the plane sat on the ground because Great Whale River was stormed in. Three hours later we returned to Montreal. We spent the night there and returned to the airport by 8 a.m. I left my bags at the airport and took only the bare necessities and checked into a plush airport hotel – only to realize that all my credit cards were in my luggage. I, of course, was not going to need them where I was going. So there I was, in the Airport Hilton, or its equivalent, in my best designer bush clothes, a pair of cords over my arm, underwear and toothbrush in my pocket, and no ID. The hotel wanted cash. I checked in and sat in my lovely room for a short time. I started to pace around the hotel trying

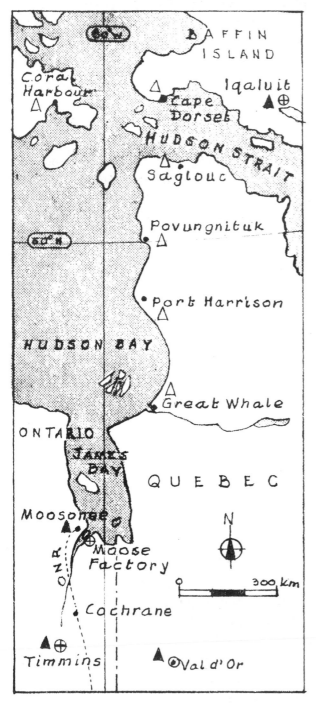

to anticipate what was ahead of me and figure out how I was going to handle the situation. It wasn't long before I noticed I was being followed.

For about an hour, the hotel security trailed fifty paces behind me. I went back to my room and phoned downtown to the regional nursing officer. I asked her to call the hotel and tell the management who I was and what I was doing there and to get them to call off the security. I was restless and started pacing the halls again. When I finally returned to my room, a huge basket of fruit was waiting for me. That was the last I saw of the security fellow.

The next morning, the plane got as far as Great Whale River. Being right on Hudson Bay, with the wind howling and the snow blowing, it was very cold and very damp. (Although it was warmer than Sioux, I was freezing because of the dampness, and I never did warm up during my month long stay along the Hudson Bay coast.) I stayed overnight at the Whale Nursing Station and I travelled on to POV. Connie Sweet, the nurse-in-charge from Whale, was in POV to do my orientation. Due to my delay in getting there, she got on the plane as I got off. We said hello on the airstrip. She told me Janet Cross had been briefed and wished me good luck. Then she disappeared onto the plane.

Janet had worked in the obstetrics and gynaecology area of the Moose Factory Hospital and would be in POV with me for the month. She had a wonderful rapport with the community as she had been there as a bridesmaid in a wedding the previous summer.

Janet also knew how to handle the volumes of paperwork required for an interprovincial medivac. Basically, she was the nurse/administrator and medivac specialist, while I dealt with all the political stuff. It turned out to be a good match.

When I arrived, I discovered that the provincial replacement doctor and his wife (who was also a nurse) were living in the doctor's trailer behind the nursing station. The Quebec nursing supervisor for the area was also there with them. Dr.Rejean Berubé and his wife had come to POV for Christmas to replace the provincial doctor who had taken over the federal nursing station. I don't think they ever expected to get caught up in all the political machinations that played out at the local level in POV. I explained my situation to Dr. Berubé and outlined the marching orders I had been given. Three days later, we all agreed that life is short: we would be political until 5 p.m. and then we would socialize. There was no animosity among us. We all realized we were caught in a much bigger web than we could control.

* * *

Strange as it may seem, what made life easier, in some respects, was the fact that just before I arrived, full phone service had gone out. We could receive calls, such as the daily one from the regional office in Montreal, asking us, "Are they (the provincial people) out yet?" However, we couldn't call out for advice, and in the event of an emergency, we had to rely on our own judgment. (It wasn't until a few days before we left POV that Bell sent in a plane. Without a word to anyone, two men walked up to the admin office, hit the reset button, and immediately, full phone service was restored. They got back on the plane and left.)

Unable to call out had proved helpful in our efforts to help a certain young woman. She had come to Janet at the nursing station in great distress, seeking shelter from her husband who had been beating her. Having previously treated the effects of spousal abuse, I was sympathetic to her situation. We knew that even if we could call out, we were not likely to get approval for sending her out. Aware that there were no planes for the next few days, we let her stay in the station until we could figure out a solution. Fearful of her husband's violent nature, she walked around the station several times every night and constantly checked to make sure the doors were locked.

During her stay with us, two sick babies were brought to the station suffering from bronchiolitis, which is common in the North at that time of the year. The mothers wear their *amoutis* (parkas) with their babies in the back. When inside, they get too hot and then they walk out into the freezing cold to get cooled off. In the process, the lungs of the children go into bronchospasm, which causes severe respiratory distress. Since we had to organize a medivac for the two babies, we decided to put our terrified woman on the plane as well. We knew she had relatives at a settlement farther south and I said we would get her to Great Whale River, but she would be on her own from there.

Her husband was in a rage looking for her, so getting her on the plane was an ordeal. Although we were under the cover of darkness, we still hid her beneath a blanket on a sled. It was pulled by one of the three snowmobiles we had to go back and forth between the plane and the station, carrying Janet and the two babies, as well as the medivac supplies. She was driven right to the airplane stairway where I was waiting. She jumped out from under the blanket and frantically climbed aboard. Meanwhile, her husband, expecting that she might try to escape from him, was on his own Ski-Doo tearing between the station and the plane. When he realized that she was already aboard the plane, he desperately tried to get to her, but couldn't, because I was guarding the door at the top of the stairs.

Once again, my six-foot stature came in handy, because with all the down and duffel I was wearing, I completely filled the airplane doorway. While he hollered at her from below, I yelled to her over my shoulder. "Do you want to talk to him?" The terrified woman cowered in the plane and pleaded with me not to let him by. I told him in no uncertain terms to "buzz off." I was in high adrenalin mode, with little fear. Only later, did it occur to me that I could have sustained considerable damage. What I also did not know was that there were about ten Inuit men standing on the ice, just outside the light of the plane, ready to pounce on the husband if he laid a hand on me or his wife.

Two days later, I received a call from Inukjuak, farther south on the coast, where the escaped woman had finally landed. She thanked me, and she said she had just had her hair cut and was eager to begin a new life, free from the terror. Apparently, the POV community knew about the drama that had preceded her departure and had taken up a collection of money for her to start her new life.

* * *

Every night during the Christmas holiday week, there was a dance at the community hall. Janet and I went the first night. There was no heat in the hall, but with almost everyone wearing a parka, it wasn't needed. We could see steam coming out the windows and the door of the building. They had a square-dance caller and an accordion player. After watching the first few rounds, I realized this was basic stuff so one of the pilots from Austin Airways and I decided to join in. Since the dance was called in Inuktitut, we were about two beats behind everyone else. Once we got going it was great fun. My dancing partner was about my height, and the Inuit fellows were about my shoulder-height, give or take a little. We were doing fine until it was "allemande left" time. I almost got my head lopped off because the Inuit men's arms couldn't reach over my head. We all had a great laugh.

I had made the mistake of wearing my thermals under my cords and by the second square dance, I was soaking wet. At one point when I was joking with one of the men, I tripped over my own feet and landed on the floor. With my underwear so wet, I couldn't bend my knees to get up. It finally took three men using a lever action at my feet to get me upright. Even though it must have looked very funny, the women told their husbands they shouldn't have laughed at the nurse. Having learned from that experience, I dressed lightly for the dance the following night. Again, I had a great time. By the third night, I crashed, having decided that I had better start pacing myself a little slower, as we had to be up for 9 a.m. clinic or possibly for emergencies during the night.

We had invited our provincial colleagues for Christmas and New Year's dinners. (Remember this battle was political, not personal, and these were very fine people.) Christmas dinner was a remarkable sight, as our Quebec friends had hit the kitchen and cooked up a storm. I knew how to do turkey, potatoes and gravy but they added the "crème de la crème" with sauces and all sorts of exotic dishes. For five people, there was one bottle of wine that had been sent up from Whale by Connie Sweet. The atmosphere and the food were marvellous as we dined with low light and candles on the table. Now you try to explain how one suffers in the high North!

Connie had also sent up a Christmas tree for us. Although it was the saddest thing I had ever seen, with only about six branches on it, Janet duly decorated it. On her next trip to Moose, she brought back a "real" tree that was tall and full, which we put in the living room and decorated.

The New Year's Eve dance was quite an affair. Already I was aware that I was the only woman in the nursing station without a dress. When I got to the party, I discovered that I was the only woman in the hall without a dress. My fancy Ports blouse looked pretty sad in comparison with the high fashion from Montreal in the room. (POV was a relatively rich community due to all the carvers and other artists who lived there. It had a French and an English school and a very active co-op for the artisans.)

The evening proceeded in the usual manner with all kinds of dancing and games. Just after midnight there was to be some entertainment. When the stage curtains opened, my jaw dropped, for there stood thirty Inuit girls in full Scottish regalia: kilts, sporrans and lace blouses. As the accordionist played, jigs and reels were danced one after another in precise formation. I was in total amazement. When I inquired where these young people had learned all the dances, I learned that the Hudson's Bay manager had married a local woman, and the previous summer, he had taken her to Scotland where she had learned the dances. Upon her return, she taught them to the young women in the community. Whenever I think of POV, the Inuit-Scottish dancers stand out as a highlight for me.

* * *

After the holiday break, it was back to business in the clinic. When two more babies with bronchiolitis had to be medivac'd out, I told Janet we had to get on top of the situation. That evening, I asked our interpreter to go to the radio station and request that all the babies under one year be brought to the nursing station. The interpreter organized the appointments. Of the 43 babies we examined that night, only three had normal chest sounds. We started them on antibiotics. Even though I was using my stethoscope to examine a baby, I could hear another baby wheezing out in the waiting room. He was put into the oxygen tent, given an injection of penicillin and then oral medication. About 4 a.m. we closed up and went to bed. At nine o'clock the following morning, an elderly gentleman was already in the clinic waiting room. He patiently sat there until we got ourselves together for the day.

When a mother brought a child with meningitis to the station, I called Dr. Berubé to ask if he would bring over his wife, a pediatric nurse, to help him stabilize the baby. (Up to this point, I had not called on her or the supervisor to do any clinical work.) While I ran the clinic, Janet started the paper work and medivac'd the baby out.

As usual, the plane had to stop at Whale to refuel. For five hours, the plane sat on the ground as they called all over Whale trying to find the person with the keys to the fuel pump. During the stopover, the IV froze and Janet froze. The only good thing was that the baby's temperature returned to normal because of the cold, and that is probably what saved her life. Of course, I knew none of this. Normally, Janet would have let me know when she got to Moose, which should have been five hours. When nine hours had gone by without a word from her, I was frantic, wondering where they were.

By the time I got the call from Janet, I had been pacing in the station for several hours. I had been very upset but by now I was mad! I stormed over to Austin Airways and proceeded to tear a strip off their innocent stationmaster. I paced back and forth in the waiting room, zigging and zagging between the freight boxes. I threatened to report the airline company to Ottawa if they didn't get the key situation in Whale sorted out. After I had ranted and raved for some time, I felt much better and left. By nine o'clock the next morning, five people had keys to the pumps.

* * *

"Are they out yet?" That was always the start of each daily call from the nursing office in Montreal. I assured them that Nature would take care of things. They were having trouble with the furnace and I had refused to authorize the repairs. I was certainly not going to let them freeze, but I didn't do anything about the inconvenience it imposed. They had to restart the furnace every two hours, night and day. I felt that sooner or later they would get tired of this and look for alternate living quarters. Not long after I left, that was the case, and the provincial doctor and nurse eventually moved into the new accommodations that were being built by the community.

Most of the ordinary daily workings of the nursing station in Povungnituk were interesting to me. The first thing I had looked for on my arrival was a radio. I was pleased that there was a good short-wave radio in the kitchen and that we could get the national news from CBC Montreal. The community also had a little station, which broadcast in Inuktitut all day, with the exception of the CBC news. The World at Six was on at 2 p.m., most likely from the international network. During my travels in and outside of Canada, the CBC has been my constant link to the world.

In remote areas, food is always a major topic of conversation, mainly because of the lack of availability. Janet and I would sit down to figure out what we needed. She would be on the phone to a store in Cochrane that did bush orders, and our groceries would be in town the next day via Austin Airways. I never really knew how much this all cost. The only damaged food I saw was a few potatoes that froze on the airstrip. Everything else was well wrapped, protected, and fresh.

* * *

One afternoon, near the end of my time in Povungnituk, I wanted to purchase some local carvings and needed some cash. I was directed to the local bank, which was a tiny office in the shape of an igloo. Normally, The Bay acted as the bank in these local communities. POV was an exception, in that it had its own small branch. I found only one teller who was working at her desk, with her baby in a playpen beside her. Unfortunately, the bank was out of money because The Bay hadn't made its deposits yet. So off I went to The Bay to get my cheque cashed so that I could buy the carvings.

* * *

When the two previous federal nurses had left for Saglouc, the house staff at the nursing station had basically gone "on holiday." They were supposedly on duty and continued to be paid. However, with the federal-provincial confusion, the house staff didn't know whose directions to follow. At first, I was too busy with the clinic and the politics to pay attention to the confusion. I remember one of the ways that the problem revealed itself. It was my first encounter with a "honey bucket" system. Normally, the pail should have been emptied daily but since I hadn't told anyone to do that, it kept getting closer and closer to the top. However, there was no smell as we used gallons of disinfectant. Finally, when it was not safe to sit down, I decided I had to empty it. Silly me. I thought I would leave it out on the front step overnight and it would be easier to empty while frozen. Not so. The next morning I brought the bucket of "concrete" into the station, after I had tried to chip out the contents with no luck. It took two days for the bucket to thaw out. Eventually the caretaker decided to deal with the situation, as he could see that I was getting nowhere with it. Janet had run for cover on this occasion.

Although we faced predicaments of this sort, we seemed to have no lack of water at the station, as the truck came by daily to top up the tanks. In fact, every house in the community was topped up daily. We had running water, a washing machine – everything but a flush toilet. Do not ask me where the grey water went, as I never got that far into the workings of the station.

* * *

As the month wore down, I knew I had to write a final report on all this. By the time I was finished, I had a document that the zone nursing officer in Sioux Lookout said looked like a consultant's report. I was critical of some areas and very positive about others. This had been my first time in an Inuit community. I had felt very welcome and had learned so much. I was totally taken aback by the people's sense of independence and their ingenuity. Their warmth and friendliness made it a tremendous pleasure to work with them. Another time, I would perhaps pace myself a little slower. But with that assignment in 1975, we had a one-month deadline and lots of work to do. I wouldn't have survived without Janet's paperwork and her knowledge of the community. She made my half of the job easy.

* * *

I arrived back in Montreal full of stories, and feeling rather guilty that I hadn't cleared out the doctor's trailer. As I said before, Nature would take its course. The regional people were happy that we had reclaimed their station, even if it was only for a short time, since the transfer of health services was in progress. It was only a matter of time before the Povungnituk Station would be formally handed over to the province.

I wanted to call Miss Skov in Ottawa, to thank her for recommending me for this assignment. I wanted to tell her what a great adventure it had been. I was disappointed to learn that she had just retired. She had quietly moved back to Denmark, with no farewell party at her request.

What a wonderful Christmas this had been! I don't think I have ever worked as hard or enjoyed my time as much as I did there. I thank the people of Povungnituk for their kindness and hospitality.

J. Karen Scott graduated in 1963 with an RN from the St. Thomas Elgin General Hospital in St. Thomas, Ontario. She obtained her BScN from the University of Windsor in 1968 and completed her nurse practitioner's course at the University of Toronto in 1975. Over a twenty-five year period, Karen has had three occasions to work in the North. The first was in the Sioux Lookout Zone during which time she was seconded to Povungnituk. On the high seas, she was Chief Medical Officer aboard the CSS Hudson, which sailed out of the Bedford Institute of Oceanography in Dartmouth, Nova Scotia. While on the Hudson, Karen spent considerable time in Arctic waters and in 1981 circumnavigated the North American continent. She was the regional occupational health nurse in Yellowknife, Northwest Territories. Karen resides in Oakville, Ontario.

**Grandmother and aunt (in moss bag) of
Joanne Smith's daughter, Jodi Metsikassus (1950)**

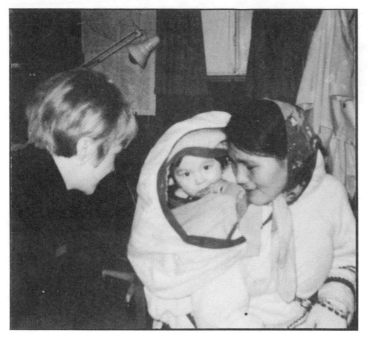

**Chris Siksik with mother and baby
in amouti (parka)**

Carolyn Anderson

**Regina Pastion CHR - 25 year award
Joanne Smith CHN, NIC - 15 year award**

Nursing Station, Old Crow, Yukon (Rose Scrivens)

Rose Scrivens with RCMP Cpl. Jim Warren, Rod Mackenzie, Const. Roger Plamonden and lobsters

**Chantelle Dunlop with Kenneth Penrose,
Lansdowne House, Ontario** (Rose Scrivens)

**Kenneth Penrose in
Landsdowne House**
(Rose Scrivens)

Medivac plane in Old Crow, Yukon (Rose Scrivens)

Dana Hawes on a snowmobile outing

Dana's birthday, Taloyoak, NWT

Elizabeth Lyle with
daughter Cathy (Dana Hawes)

"Other related duties"

Dana Hawes on the land on a camping trip

Home visit to an outpost camp (Audrey Woodget, 1963)

**George Woodget and Emile Immanoitok - tea break
during the hunt** (Audrey Woodget, 1963)

Audrey getting ready for home visits with Emile and dogs (1963)

Audrey's daughter, Karen with friends and seal (Audrey Woodget)

August Enzoe, Karen Stauffer, Judith Cathlique
(Snowdrift Nursing Station employees, 1982)

Karen Stauffer outside Snowdrift (1983)

Sister Montpetit with
Mary-Adele Bishop CHR, Rae, NWT

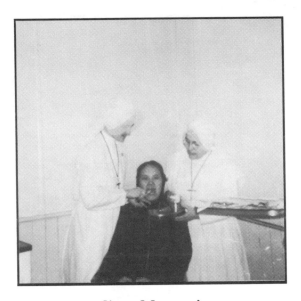

Sister Montpetit
pulling teeth (1965)

J. Karen Scott in front of Alexander Falls, Hay River, NWT

Inuit Children (Dana Hawes)

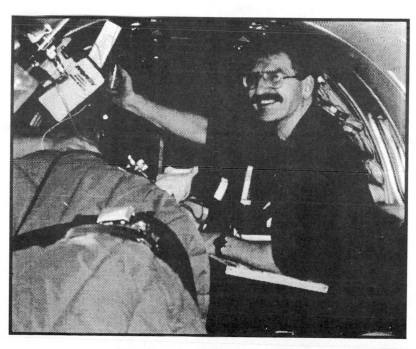

Calum Lunn in the air ambulance

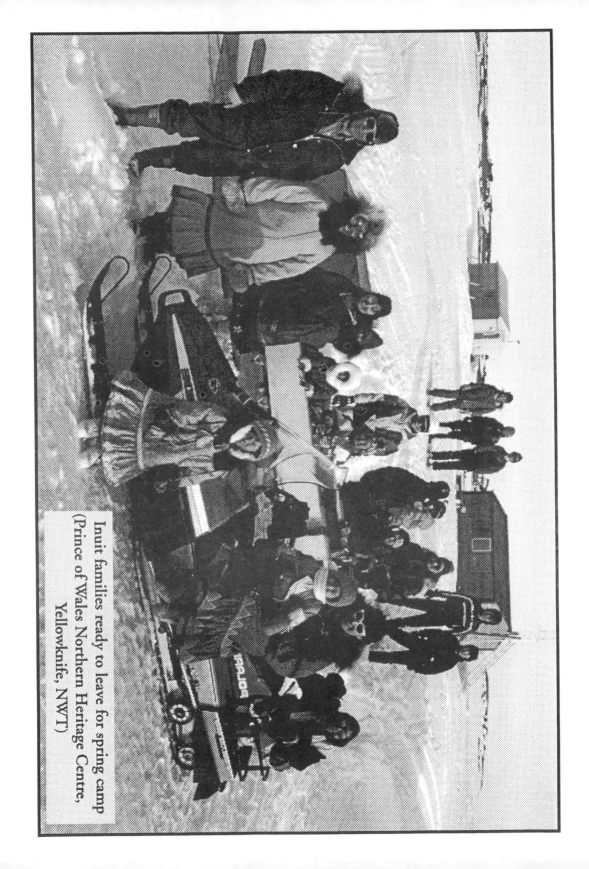

Inuit families ready to leave for spring camp
(Prince of Wales Northern Heritage Centre,
Yellowknife, NWT)

A DIFFERENT NIGHT ON CALL

Allan McCallum RN (EC), BScN, PHC NP, FNP/C(US)

One of the most memorable events during my time on the Wabassemoong (formerly Whitedog) Reserve occurred one night in January, 2000. Being on call was a major part of our job, and it was my turn to be on standby. As usual, I sat at my desk and charted on the files of clients I had seen earlier in the day.

At nine o'clock in the evening, I received my first call. My heart always jumped when I heard the phone ring, as you never knew what to expect. You had to be prepared for anything. I picked up the phone. It was one of the community members who said that there had been an accident and that someone had been hit by a car and was lying at the side of the road.

As a nurse, you often think the worst. I quickly called an ambulance and gave them the details. I ran out of the examination room, down the hall and grabbed my emergency bags. I made sure I had everything I might need at the accident site. I threw on my coat, locked the door to the health centre and headed for the jeep. I remember it was very cold outside and I could feel the wind against my face. I recall thinking that I really didn't want to be out in this weather. Getting to the jeep was always a challenge due to the reserve dogs jumping all over me, looking for food.

I loaded everything into the jeep. With my adrenaline pumping, I drove down the washboard road as many thoughts passed through my mind. Could I handle the situation? Would this person be alive? It was dark and I had a terrible time trying to locate the site. I had never been good with directions and I hoped I could find it. As I slowed down for a bend in the road, I saw someone waving at me. I braked, stopped and pulled down the window to get a view of the person walking towards the jeep. It was one of our community health representatives, who informed me that I needed to go to the bottom of the hill. Heading down, I could see a group of people standing close together, waiting for my arrival. I pulled over to the side of the road. I grabbed my emergency bags and pushed through the people, expecting to see a person lying on the ground. To my amazement, what I saw was a small tan Labrador puppy! The owner approached me and begged me to take care of her dog. She thought that I might not have come if I had known it was a dog that had been struck by a car.

At first, I didn't know what to do. My only thought was, "I am nurse, not a veterinarian. How am I supposed to care for this puppy in the dark and at the side of the road? How am I going to explain this to our zone officer and to the other nurses?"

I asked one of the band members to carry our patient to the nearest home and once inside, I cancelled the ambulance. Because the pup appeared to have a fractured leg, I opened the emergency bags looking for bandages and something for a splint. The dog had a rapid heart rate and moaned when I touched it. It didn't even lift its head. I was concerned that this was more serious than what I could handle. However, I did not want to convey to the family my concern that their puppy was not going to make it. When I finished wrapping its leg, I cleaned the wounds on the back of his head and down his neck. I instructed someone to call a veterinarian and said that the puppy needed to be transported into town. I wrapped him in a blanket, carried him outside and put him into a car. As I watched the car drive off down the road, I stood in silence for a moment. I prayed that something could be done for this little patient.

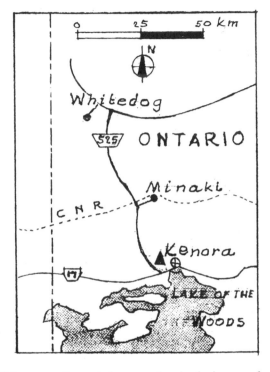

When I returned to the health centre, all I could think of was how I was going to explain this to the others. Despite the cold, I sat in the driver's seat and rehearsed what I was going to say and do. Eventually, I jumped out of the jeep and went inside. I restocked the bags and plugged in the kettle to make myself a steamy hot chocolate. Before I could take one sip of my drink, the phone rang again – another emergency. I just shook my head and told the other nurse that I was off again.

Not all nights were like this. The most stressful part of my job was the isolation and being on call. Working in the North has taught me valuable lessons, both personally and professionally. I think of my experiences as a journey, not knowing where it will lead.

Allan McCallum graduated in 1991 from St. Clair College of Applied Arts and Technology in Windsor, Ontario. In Detroit, Michigan, he practised in medical-surgical, maternal-child and emergency units. He worked as a float nurse and in the Oncology Unit of the National Defense Medical Centre in Ottawa, Ontario. In 1999, Allan completed his degree and obtained his certificate as a Primary Health Care Nurse Practitioner. He worked for the Medical Services Branch of Health Canada, and taught at the University of Manitoba in the Faculty of Nursing. He has worked in Fort Frances as a nurse practitioner at the Gizhewaadiziwin Aboriginal Health Access Centre. At present, he is a nurse practitioner with the Canadian Mental Health Association in Windsor where he is involved in a pilot project for the Ministry of Health for Ontario.

MY FRIEND ANGELO – WHO WAS HE?

Ephie Carrier

"What do you mean – Angelo is in jail? What did he do?"

"I don't know. All I know is that he's in jail. Could you find out what it's all about?" one of his friends asked.

"What happened? His Italian temper finally got him in trouble?" She looked at me teary-eyed and said nothing.

In November, 1974, Angelo Tarcisius DiStefano had arrived in Inuvik, having been hired in Ottawa as a surgeon to practise in the Inuvik General Hospital. As the acting zone director, I had received a telex from our headquarters in Edmonton a couple of weeks before, advising us of his arrival. The medical staff was pleased to have a replacement for our surgeon who had gone to Ghana. Angelo's sixteen-month stay in Inuvik was tumultuous, and his emotional manipulations were frequent. Of course, he had his followers and his adversaries, yet the medical staff seemed to approve of him. His "party" stories about exploits in Africa and the pictures of horrible "cases" in his practices were numerous. But, strangely, he was never in the photographs.

Angelo was well-accepted in the community as the "surgeon." He performed all the normal functions of a surgeon in the only Canadian hospital north of the Arctic Circle from skin surgery to repairing a stab wound to the heart. Many cases that required specialists were sent to Edmonton. Consultants visited Inuvik regularly, and at all times, Angelo was part of their discussions.

During the time of Angelo's stay in Inuvik, the RCMP investigated a double murder on a tugboat in Norman Wells and came to certain conclusions. As a surgeon who was accepted by the court as an expert in surgery and pathology, Angelo nullified some of the RCMP's evidence. The police suspected, however, that he was wrong. Since they couldn't refute an "expert," they had to search for other evidence, which they eventually found.

Things began to surface. The nurse who was in charge of the operating room reported what she thought to be unusual behaviour on Angelo's part. She shared her doubts about his training, so I showed her all the documentation I had received about him, including a provincial certification. (A professional qualified anywhere in Canada could practise with the federal government in the Territories.) At that time, we had no director of nursing services, and I was not prepared to broach the matter with the Chief of Medical Staff without solid evidence to go on.

81

In the fall of 1975, an obstetrics and gynaecology professor from the University of British Columbia came to Inuvik as a locum. He had written several textbooks and hundreds of articles for scientific journals and was a world authority on reproduction and population. He, too, had concerns about Angelo. Nevertheless, he was circumspect. He advised a couple of senior nurses to fly to Edmonton if any kind of surgery was needed, but he wouldn't elaborate.

It was on the evening of February 14, 1976, that Angelo's friend came over to tell me that Angelo was in jail. My first reaction was that there had been a mistake. How could our surgeon be in jail? "Just hang on," I said. "I'll call the RCMP. I represent National Health and Welfare here, and I should be able to find out what's going on with one of our staff." Although the police admitted that they had him under arrest, they said they could not discuss the reason. I was flabbergasted. I phoned the regional director who told me that he knew Angelo had been arrested, but he did not know why. He was aware that it was an Interpol investigation and advised us to ensure that Angelo did not practise medicine in the zone until this was cleared up. Angelo's friend went home in tears.

Soon afterwards, I received a phone call from the Inuvik member of the NWT assembly, who wanted to know about Angelo's detention. A few hours later, a phone call came from the Executive Assistant to the Minister of Health and Welfare Canada, who wanted the details for the Minister. She said he would be in the House on the following Monday and had to be briefed. I contacted the Chief of Medical Staff to apprise him of the events, as I knew them. He was stunned, having no idea why Angelo was in jail; there had been no complaints that he knew of. He would immediately inform the other doctors. We decided to get together the next morning, which was Sunday.

Before our meeting, I went to the police headquarters and asked to see Angelo. He was inside a large dog cage (a temporary cell for use in isolated areas). He looked terrible. The police had provided only the minimum of amenities. (Seeing him like this, I remembered how he had thwarted their murder investigation in Norman Wells.) I chatted with him but he was subdued and untalkative. He claimed that he did not know why he was there. The RCMP on duty informed me there was a bail hearing for Angelo early in the week. Some members of the medical staff were furious at what the police had done to their colleague. They thought there was a mistake somewhere. Informed of the bail hearing, they agreed to be there to find out what was going on. In the meantime, nothing could be done for Angelo in jail.

On the day of the hearing, the court was filled to capacity. The judge sat on his dais above everyone. Angelo and his lawyer were at the allocated table, and the RCMP officers sat with the crown lawyer. The young lawyer pleaded for Angelo's bail, extolling his record in Inuvik, and he explained how his work was vital to the community of the western Arctic. "I'll hear argument from the police," the judge said, as he made a note.

The RCMP Staff Sergeant was sworn in. "Your Honour," he began, "I will now present for evidence, based on the identification of ten fingerprints from Interpol, compared to ten fingerprints of the accused, that this man, Angelo Tarcisius DiStefano, was arrested fourteen times between 1956 and 1965 and convicted nine times on charges of fraud, forgery, impersonation and embezzlement. He is wanted in Rome to face charges of impersonating a medical doctor, practising without a license, forgery and fraud. He was jailed for one year in France, for forgery in 1963." The officer shuffled his papers and continued to present evidence from a thick file.

I did not hear any more. Instead, I turned and whispered to the Chief of Medical Staff, "You know, the records we have indicate that was at the University of Rome taking medical and surgical training during that time!" He got up, saying, "Let's go, I've heard enough." I stayed, however, and listened to the judge grant bail, with conditions. Angelo was not to leave Inuvik, and was to report to the RCMP twice daily.

We had a couple of get-togethers for Angelo, but he had lost his spirit. He said this was a plot from the Red Brigade in Italy to punish him for leaving them and failing to finance them. Two weeks later, the RCMP escorted him to Montreal where Interpol agents from Italy picked him up. Subsequently, all his medical and surgical work was reviewed by a board of surgeons in Edmonton. No major adverse implications were found.

Months later, Angelo's friend told me that she had received a letter from him. We were all eager to find out how he was. She said that he was working in Finland as a specialist in Arctic medicine. True? Who knows? Maybe. But who was he? We never did find out.

Ephie Carrier graduated in 1968 from the University of Saskatchewan in Hospital Administration. He was acting Zone Director in Inuvik from 1974 to 1977 and has been a hospital administrator in many isolated areas. Ephie presently resides in New Brunswick.

ADVENTURES OF A NORTHERN NURSE

Dana Hawes RN

My trek to the Arctic began in 1994 when I decided to leave Calgary, Alberta where I worked as an emergency nurse at Foothills Hospital. I wanted to find a new way of being a nurse. Although emergency nursing in a trauma centre in a large Canadian hospital had been challenging and rewarding, I was restless and bored. I accepted a contract in Taloyoak (Spence Bay) for a month and I never really left. Whenever I thought I would leave the North, the North always called me back. Taloyoak is 200 miles north of the Arctic Circle, 700 miles north of the treeline, in the Kitikmeot region.

It was a beautiful sunny day in May when I left Calgary, taking only a backpack and a duffel bag. My duffel bag was green, and those who knew me for the next few years fondly labeled it my "green dresser." I lived out of it for so long it became my only constant possession. I still own that "green dresser."

As this part of the world was unknown to me, I was apprehensive about my decision. I hoped I could meet the challenge of working in health centres with the nearest doctor or hospital hundreds of miles away. The health centres had very minimal diagnostics such as x-ray machines and laboratory equipment. I would be required to learn how to use the equipment, as well as to read x-rays, to obtain specimens and to use a microscope in order to make correct diagnoses. I would also prescribe and dispense medication. I was aware that in the event of a blizzard (and in the winter there are many) a medivac plane might not be able to come to my aid for days. I prayed I would be able to meet the tremendous expectations ahead.

My first stop was Cambridge Bay where I had a few days of orientation. When I arrived there, it was afternoon, around zero degrees, bright and sunny, with snow piled six feet high in places. Spring thaw had started, and there were rivers running everywhere. Back home in Calgary, gumboots had certainly not been fashionable and I had never owned any. I was very grateful to be given my first pair by a kind nurse who felt sorry for this naïve southerner. I spent three days learning about my new world. By then, I was really scared.

I arrived in Taloyoak and met some of the greatest nurses I have ever encountered: Marianne Ewence, Natalie Morin and Val Walker. Natalie was leaving for holidays and I was there to relieve her. I quickly jumped in to become familiar with the ways of the local folks. For instance, one of the first things I had to learn was that, to the Inuit people, the raising of an eyebrow means "yes" and the wrinkling of the nose means "no."

Marianne was a midwife at the birthing project. Healthy women with low risk pregnancies did not go to the hospital to have their babies. We would deliver them at the centre.

My only experience with birthing had been in nursing school. An emergency nurse knows nothing about birthing babies. I was up for many nights with a labouring woman, and with Marianne's expertise, I became more confident and less uneasy.

Summer in the Inuit culture is a joyous time. The Inuit are happiest when out on the land in tents. I quickly felt accepted by the local people, and on many occasions, I was privileged to be invited to their camps for tea and bannock. They would provide local transportation, a 4-wheel ATV, which often carried five or six other people. Since it is the only means of transportation, the RCMP turned a blind eye to this traffic violation. In these northern communities, there is often only one dirt path that leads to the airport and it passes by the dump on the way. There is usually one RCMP vehicle, but some health centres might have another vehicle. People travel by ATV in the summer and by snowmobile in the winter. There are no traffic rules, no stop signs or traffic lights. As my first summer in Taloyoak went by with its twenty-four hour daylight, I grew to love the people and their ways.

* * *

I remember one night when I was called to help a new mother with a cranky infant. Although this is natural for a new baby, I felt nervous and agreed to meet the mother at the health centre. (There is no ambulance service for local people; they must find their own way to the health centre.)

When I arrived, the child was breathing, but lethargic. We had delivered this baby three weeks earlier and it was healthy. Its heart rate was 60 (120-160 is the norm for this age), which meant that we had to begin CPR immediately. I knew that the medivac plane would not arrive for hours. I started an IV, administered oxygen and flicked the baby's heels for the next eight hours, while I monitored its cardiac status. Sweat ran down my arms as I tried to reassure the mom that everything would be okay. I did not let her know that I was petrified. We were all relieved when Pat O'Connor arrived with the medivac plane. The child was taken to the University of Alberta Hospital in Edmonton with a diagnosis of RSV, a respiratory infection that is fatal to infants. I am thrilled to report that little Naiya recovered and is a healthy youngster today.

* * *

Another memorable event occurred during a late spring storm. An elder of the community, who had recently lost his daughter to a brain aneurysm, called to say his legs were "real sore." A blizzard raged outside and I honestly did not know if I could find my way, even though I lived only the equivalent of one block from the health centre. I eventually made it there, and so did he. The man had serious frostbite. I treated him, and gave him instructions to call me if the symptoms worsened, although I knew that there was no chance of a medivac.

I started to walk home, not knowing in which direction I was headed because the snow blinded me. The drifts were six to eight feet high and the wind howled at 80-100 km per hour. I was lost in a blizzard! No matter what direction I tried moving, I kept running into a wall of snow. My face felt as if rice was being hurled at it, and I couldn't stand up against the raging wind. Even though I knew I was only a block from safety, I truly believed I would freeze to death. On the prairies where I had been raised, I had seen blizzards – but nothing like this formidable Arctic storm. I thought I saw lights and headed towards them, hoping it was not a mirage. Only 50 metres away from me was the RCMP corporal who had gotten stuck while out on a call. His vehicle was warm and had a full tank of gas. We sat there for most of the night, until we were able to make our way in the early morning. This meant that there had been no RCMP and no nurse on call, but we were alive and well.

* * *

One November, Marianne and I decided go to Middle Lake to visit some Inuit friends for tea and bannock. The temperature was minus 60° F and we were on a snowmobile. Since it was November, when the sun is up for only about an hour, we thought we would take advantage of the magnificent sunrise at approximately 11:00 a.m. The sunrises in the high Arctic are the closest thing to heaven one may ever encounter. The bright pinks, purples and blues that reflect off the angel-white Arctic snow are burned into my memory forever. Although it is frighteningly cold, that is forgotten. Hawaii has nothing on the Arctic when it comes to sunrises and sunsets.

We were grateful for the tea and bannock given to us when we arrived at Middle Lake. The local people were pleased that the *Kablunaks* (the white people) would actually take time to visit. If we had the courage to venture out of our comfort zone, they treated us like royalty. We got laughed at when we admitted we were freezing because the Inuit don't get cold. As we were so far north of the treeline, a warm fire was out of the question. In fact, in those days, most Inuit had never seen wood or trees. Some of the better-off folk had access to naphtha gas, but the average family did not. The Inuit were swathed in caribou clothes and *kamiks* (caribou boots).

On our way home after tea, we found ourselves hopelessly lost in a blizzard on the tundra. I was supposed to catch a plane to Gjoa Haven and I was late. That was the least of my worries. I was beyond that: I was frozen. As luck would have it, we smelled something rancid. It was the dump! We followed the smell and made our way to Taloyoak, to the local RCMP who were frantic about the "missing nurses." They got me to the airport (an Atco trailer) as fast as they could, considering the weather. Still wearing my large red parka and my snowmobile regalia, I boarded the plane that was being held for me. No one paid any attention, as there are no fashion codes in the Arctic. Being warm is more important.

As I began my time as nurse-in-charge in Gjoa Haven, a community of approximately 1000 people, I became friendly with the teachers and several local people, I was invited on a weekend of camping on Koca Lake. I agreed to camp in the Arctic in November because the isolation during my lonely nights in government housing was getting to me. After a three-hour snowmobile trip, I wondered what we would do for a whole weekend. Although Gjoa Haven is very flat, we managed to find a hill where we could build a three-sided shelter. The cold Arctic wind is brutal, and with the temperature at minus 80°, I was concerned about how I would survive the weekend. I was already cold.

We were kept busy. We shovelled out the snow on three sides and then we pitched a tent. Tea was made, but I passed up the generous offer because I was so worried about having to go the bathroom. I worried about nature calling and I couldn't imagine undressing to relieve myself. (I thought I must have gone mad, as I was doing this as recreation.) Our tent looked cozy with caribou skins on the floor. We had a Coleman lantern and stove, but it was so brutally cold they only took the edge off. With all due respect to Woods, I was still beyond cold in their 5-Star sleeping bag. Meanwhile, the Inuit were in their glory.

As the weekend progressed, we busied ourselves with ice fishing, cards and meal preparations. While we played rummy, they drank tea. (I still worried about the bathroom business.) We prepared raw frozen fish. (I prayed I wouldn't get fish tapeworms, which were common.) We also had rations of pilot biscuits (thick saltine crackers), whale and caribou. I learned to appreciate raw caribou and marmalade on pilot biscuits.

By the last day, I was frozen. There was no way to measure temperature, but that did not matter; it was just damn cold. On our three-hour trip back to town on the back of a *komatik* (a homemade Inuit sled), I wondered if I would die of the cold. (Apparently, it feels good, in the end, to freeze to death but I did not feel good.) I kept seeing a mirage of lights and I feared the trip would never end. I am proud of myself because I never complained. The Inuit love this life. This is their world and I wanted to experience it. It had been my choice.

When we finally reached home, I thanked them very much. I had really dug deep to find the joy in their world. They are the hardiest people I have ever known. Afterwards, I shook in my bed for hours, with every joint in my body aching. I knew then that I was a *Kablunak* "softie," but I had tried.

* * *

In remote communities, food is hard to come by. The Inuit obtain theirs by hunting and fishing, and they were always more than generous in sharing their cherished food with me. Even today, I am thankful at every meal for the abundance and availability of things to eat in the South. I have also learned to be grateful for warm clothing that I can buy easily at the store. The Inuit still make their clothing.

For a nurse who lives in an isolated community, food becomes an obsession. There is usually a local Northern Store, formerly The Hudson's Bay. Once a year, supplies arrive on a barge that has travelled through the Inside Passage. When the meagre goods (all non-perishable) reach us, they are frequently outdated. When the weather is exceptionally cold, the barge freezes into the ice, with the result that there is nothing for the year. Then the prices soar.

One Christmas in the mid 90s, four of us paid $68 for a 12-pound turkey and $17 for five pounds of potatoes that had been frozen during transport. We were that hungry for our kind of food. One summer, we paid $40 for a 7-pound watermelon, which we sliced up for the local children. After all, what is summer without watermelon. On rare occasions, fresh fruits or vegetables were brought in by airfreight, sometimes costing up to $3 a pound to transport. Often, they had frozen and thawed several times before we got them. When the RCMP plane would come in to take a prisoner to jail, the nurses were asked if we would like anything from Yellowknife. Fresh fruit and vegetables and Tim Horton doughnuts would be the highlight of the month! I remain grateful to the RCMP pilots. Although I still am overwhelmed in a southern grocery store, I now actually enjoy shopping. (I certainly didn't before I went north.) I cringe when southern folks complain about produce in their modern supermarkets for they have no idea how fortunate they are.

* * *

I remember an instance when I was in Gjoa Haven. A young child had been sent to the Yellowknife Hospital a week or so earlier for a respiratory illness. I had a call from a physician in Yellowknife with his instructions because they were sending the child home on the plane. The physician had recently come to Yellowknife from the United States. He was young and had just become a "real doctor." He had no idea about life in the North: he knew little about the people, the land, the hardships or the culture. His instructions were to make sure this child got an abundance of fruit and vegetables. I laughed and asked if he had any idea where we were and what was available. He said that he didn't really care, only that these were his orders. I told him that there were no real stores and that, even if the plane could bring in a few fresh items, the prices would be impossibly high. (For instance, a head of frozen lettuce was somewhere in the neighborhood of $8-$10 and the choices among these gems were minimal.)

I explained to him that in this child's family there were six more children, as well as twelve other people, and that the extended family lived in a small two-room house with one bed. (Housing is in perpetually short supply, prices are phenomenal and families must often live together.) He then asked if it wasn't my job as the nurse in the community to ensure that all these children got what they required. I informed him that there were approximately 350 children under the age of six living in these conditions. However, if he would provide the funds, we would be glad to feed them all. He was outraged.

As it turned out, when I was back in Taloyoak a few months later, I discovered that this physician was the one who would be coming to town to work at the health centre. When I picked him up from the plane on a cold, dark February afternoon, he was wearing a fashionable, fluorescent green ski suit and carrying cross-country skis. I took him to the health centre, showed him the room where he would be working and I continued on my own to the public health clinic.

He eventually wanted to know who would cook for him. I couldn't help but laugh as I explained to him that he was responsible for bringing his own food and surviving like the rest of us. I offered him the health centre van and I pointed him in the direction of the Northern Store. He came back empty-handed, declaring that there was no way he was paying those unbelievable prices for that "crap." He then asked Natalie, the other nurse, and me if we had any extra food. We gave him some apples (he had no idea what these treasures meant to us), a box of Cheerios and some milk (another delicacy). He also asked if we had some cheese and crackers for a snack. (Even if we had, we were not going to be that generous.)

During the physician's two-day stay, he complained that it was impossible to do his job with minimal diagnostics and no high tech equipment. We reminded him that this was our daily routine and that he would now have to use all those "wonderful" clinical skills he had learned in medical school. His arrogance subsided, and he left our community, choosing never again to do clinics in the isolated outposts. I suggested to him that he learn about the North, the people and their culture if he were going to stay. I never received an apology from him.

In retrospect, his plan of cross-country skiing was equally unrealistic. During February, high in the Arctic, there are 24 hours of darkness. The tundra is covered with boulder-size rocks, and there isn't much snow. Any snow that falls is like Styrofoam frozen so hard that, when you walk on it, it actually echoes in the Arctic quiet. It is so quiet that it almost hurts your ears. Never before or since have I experienced such absolute silence as I have on a cold dark Arctic night. The only sound will be from sled dogs tied up on the sea ice, howling from hunger. It is an eerie, pathetic assault on your auditory senses. This is not the place for cross-country skiing.

* * *

One cold, Arctic morning, an Inuit woman arrived at the health centre and requested her baptism. Her first language was Inuktitut and, like many of the Inuit, she spoke little English. She had difficulty communicating her need for her baptism. When I told her that Father Tony, the Catholic priest, made frequent visits and that there was an Anglican minister in town, she became frustrated and demanding. With my minimal Inuktitut and her broken English, we had a huge communication problem. Normally, an interpreter would be at the nursing station, but not that day. "What medical term sounds like baptism?" I pondered. I started rhyming words in my head. "Bap" rhymes with "pap." So I asked her if she wanted her Pap test. Eagerly, she replied that that was it. (She was the first woman I had ever encountered who was excited about a Pap test.) I mentioned the incident to the local priest, a grand fellow with a great sense of humor. He appreciated the funny side of the story.

* * *

As winter turns to spring, and eventually to summer, the tundra fills with beautiful lichen and flowers, and the mosquitoes are out in full force. The sun is up for 24 hours and the weather turns warm. One afternoon, a young woman, about 20 years old, came to the centre in need of a certain antibiotic for a particular condition. With this antibiotic, it is important not to spend too much time in direct sunlight. I explained this to her and, on her way out, I cautioned her, "Now don't forget to watch the sun."

While I was on call that night, my phone rang at ten o'clock. It was the young woman who said she was feeling fine, but asked, "How long do I have to watch the sun?"

"For ten days until your antibiotics are done." I replied.

"You mean I have to stay up for 10 days, night and day, and look at the sun?" she exclaimed. I made it clear that she didn't actually need to look at the sun. We both had a good laugh. I should have known better because, by that time, I had been in the Arctic for about five years and I knew that, in the Inuit culture, *everything* is taken literally.

* * *

When I first arrived in the Arctic, it was the beginning of summer. A kind, local lady asked if I would like to go out on the land and make a fire with Heather. Although I was thrilled to accept the invitation, I wondered how on earth we were going to make a fire. We both jumped on her ATV and headed out on the land. When we stopped, I asked her if we had forgotten to pick up Heather, or was Heather going to meet us. I had no idea who Heather was and assumed that Heather was one of her friends. My new friend burst out laughing and asked me if I really thought Heather was a person. She explained that heather, which is found growing on the tundra, is used to build a fire. I soon became familiar with this moss-like plant. We enjoyed a wonderful fire and a cup of tea. After that, there were many laughs at my expense.

* * *

Along with all the joy of being with the people of Canada's Arctic, come heartaches that can wear you down. There is horrible poverty, hunger and abuse. The Inuit were nomadic and lived on the land in igloos until the 1960s and they had not been exposed to our communication sources or the media. They also had no experience in handling money. How frequently I have heard them criticized for not saving their money. Yet, until recently, there were no banks, bankcards, Visa cards, or even stores where they could be used. Money is relatively new to them. Only two generations ago, they were concerned mainly with basic survival.

Their food came from hunting and fishing, their clothing was made from animal skins, and their shelter was a snowhouse in the winter and a tent in the summer. While many of their elders have lived in the traditional manner, the younger generation has been expected, by non-native people, to adapt to southern culture. As a result, there are many struggles because of the huge generation gap that exits. The Inuit have come far in a short time; nevertheless, I am not sure "our way" is better for them. We have forced them to live as we do, but with very limited resources and little understanding of their culture on our part.

For thousands of years, the Inuit lived without clocks. Now we expect them to live on a time schedule – like that of our white society. In the summer, it is not uncommon to see kids outside playing all night long, since it is as light at three in the morning, as it is at three in the afternoon. How do they know if it is day or night? Really, what is the difference if the children are out at 3 a.m. or 3 p.m.? For them, there are just two seasons: light and dark. I have often heard white government workers criticize the Inuit for their ways, and I have never figured out why we think our way is better. I conclude that it is because we think the Inuit don't fit into our schedule. I often ask why they should.

* * *

I once treated a 13 year-old boy with recurrent tonsillitis. I went to great lengths to explain to him and his mother that he would have to have his tonsils removed. I was surprised by his eagerness and wondered if my communication skills were accurate. In my experience, hospitals and surgery are scary for this age group. When I questioned him about his positive reaction, he told me that he had never been on a plane and had never seen Yellowknife. He had always wanted to see the big city. (At that time, Yellowknife had a population of approximately 17,000.) His goal was to get there, and he hoped I would make sure that he had his surgery. When he boarded the plane, he was as excited as a child on Christmas Eve.

Upon his return, he reported on his big adventure with great excitement in his eyes. He had never seen streets, pavement, trees or stores: all the things we take for granted. I tried to imagine what it must have been like. He had never experienced a restaurant, a hospital, cars, trucks or traffic lights; he had never seen that many people. When I asked him what his favorite things were, he exclaimed, "McDonalds and Wal-Mart." After that, his goal in life was to live in Yellowknife. His surgery was no big deal for him, and he didn't give a second thought to the pain. Now when I watch parents in our culture become hysterical when their child has a minor illness, I have a difficult time feeling empathy. The North has changed me forever.

* * *

During my time in Taloyoak, I had the privilege of being friends with a special Inuit lady, Mary Omeagmuq, the housekeeper at the health centre. She asked if she could phone me and I said yes. She fondly became known as Me Mary because every time she called she would say, "Hi! This me, Mary." I had to keep a certain amount of professional distance so I couldn't be a friend to all the local ladies. Mary, however, was special. She came over to my house with bannock in hand; I had made her a loaf of bread. (Leavened bread was hard to come by, but I had a bread maker.) When she told me how privileged she felt to be in my home, I asked her why. She confided to me that at the age of 10 she had been invited into my house as a Brownie – and she was now 38.

During our frequent visits, either at her house or mine, Mary shared her stories of being raised in an igloo. Our worlds were very different. I couldn't believe that I was actually hearing, first-hand, from a woman of her age what it was like to be an Inuit child in the 1960s. For her part, she couldn't believe that, as friends, I was a "nurse" and she, in her mind only, a "lowly Inuit woman." She was a big influence in my life and I owe much to her. When I asked Mary her favourite food that *Kablunaks* ate, she told me it was ham. The next Christmas, I had a ham flown in from Yellowknife for her and her family, and I left it on their porch.

Once when I was going south to Calgary and Vancouver to see my family, I asked Mary if there was anything she wanted. She answered, "A map of the world." I purchased the biggest one I could find, and it hung on her living-room wall. We spent an afternoon placing stickpins where all the white folks she knew came from. When I asked whether or not she had ever been out of Yellowknife, she told me that she once had gone to Edmonton for medical reasons. I asked if she had been able to see any of my beloved province and discovered that the boarding home had taken them on a tour out to the country. I inquired as to what she remembered about my land. "The smell of cow shit," she replied. That is what stuck out in her mind. I laughed myself silly. Mary was a very special lady to whom I shall forever be indebted.

* * *

Another incident that I will never forget is my first experience ice fishing with the Inuit. Our clerk and interpreter, Annie Buchan, a wonderful human being, invited me to join her for a day of ice fishing. She promised to show me some important survival skills. The fact that I didn't possess any fishing equipment was not a problem; she assured me that I didn't need any of that fancy *Kablunak* stuff. We headed out on our ATVs. Even though it was June, the ice remained many feet deep. When we stopped out on the lake, Annie drilled holes in the ice with the brand new ice auger she had received for her birthday. I still didn't know what I was going to fish with, for I couldn't see any rods or bait.

She hauled out the ends of two hockey sticks she had scavenged from the local kids, tied on some fishing line and used white plastic from a shopping bag for bait. We caught so many land-locked char that day that we ate like kings for a week. It eventually dawned on me that I was white and, by law, needed a fishing license. I admitted my naiveté to the local RCMP, who had a good chuckle, and told me to get a license next time. I offered to share my fish with them.

* * *

After several years in the high Arctic, I decided that I should move on and try something else. I had the opportunity to be the nurse at Canada's first diamond mine, BHP, at Ekati, about 300 km north of Yellowknife. I would work a two-week in and two-week out rotation. Since there were no roads, the only way in and out was by air. The mine, which was under construction at the time, was an amazing project. It still overwhelms me to think of the huge shovels, trucks and heavy equipment. The struggles to mine diamonds in an unforgiving land, with techniques that have never been tried before, are indeed an enigma to me.

Now, I was back working in a world with Caucasians, whose stress levels were more than I could handle. I had come from an Inuit world into a white world of isolated men in a camp. The general population was frustrated due to a lack of stimulation. By most standards, the camp was impressive but the workers, who had mostly come from large cities, felt hard done by. I admit I had little sympathy for them. This was my shortcoming. Having lived in the high Arctic, I had come to realize what was important in life. As far as I was concerned, the folks south of 60 just didn't get it.

In an agreement with the government of the NWT, there was to be a large percentage of "native hire" at this mine. The aboriginals, both Inuit and First Nations, were flown into camp from their communities at no cost to them. I was aware of the enormous cultural divide and I tried to work with company officials to enlighten them on the differences. First of all, many of these employees had never been away from their home communities, let alone having lived and worked in a camp. A lot of them had never had a job and at first, needed to be told exactly what to do. Supervisors frequently became exasperated when native workers, feeling totally overwhelmed, would leave camp and never come back. Not only did they *not* fit into our world, but also their own communities often banished them for having taken on white man's ways. When I tried to explain to management what the problems were, they accused me of trying to save the North. I always knew I couldn't save the North. I had never seen any reason to try. I didn't find it needed saving.

* * *

I left the mining business for a position as a northern flight nurse stationed in Yellowknife. We flew sick or injured people from their communities to a hospital in the western Arctic or to one in the Kitikmeot region. If the patients were too ill for Stanton Regional Hospital in Yellowknife, we went to Edmonton where there are full services. Our planes were a

King Air 200 and a King Air 90, a Twin Otter for flights into exploration camps and occasionally, in the summer, a floatplane.

One incident stands out in my mind. On a cold, dark December night around 10 o'clock, I was called to an exploration camp. Apparently, the cook had been out on her snowmobile and had gone over a 12-foot embankment. There were no other details since there were no medical people on site. We fired up the Twin Otter and set off to find her. Exploration camps are temporary, with some type of shelter, often sprung structures or rudimentary plywood shacks. Because there are no permanent runways, only ice strips, there are no landing lights. Instead, flare pots, often jam cans filled with fuel, are lit and set along the landing strip. I arrived to find a snowmobile with a *komatik* waiting to take me the five miles in order to pick up the injured cook. The weather was about minus 50°. When we reached our patient, her only complaint was her "sore wrist." We bundled her up, placed her in the *komatik* and headed back for the plane. She had a badly broken wrist that we splinted with full c-spine precautions, yet never once did she complain or even wince.

* * *

In some communities, the only method of transportation is the back of the RCMP pick-up truck. At the health centre, we load our patient, who is on a stretcher, and ourselves into the back of the open pick-up. Our patients are warmly covered with a huge down sleeping bag. Some of the airports are 15-20 km from the health centre, and at 60 below, in the back of a truck, it is cold. You must be careful, as IV lines and catheters are plastic and freeze easily, and the IV fluid will also freeze in minutes.

Nursing in remote areas can be a very tiring job. You may just return from a call that has taken 10-12 hours and be called out again for another 10-12 hours. The beauty of it is the sense of freedom you have. Every day, when you go to work, you are going somewhere different. If you love to fly, it is an awesome job. The pilots of the North are the true heroes. I have never met a bush pilot who wasn't talented and conscientious. The pilots for Air Tindi, the air carrier in Yellowknife, work on call flying day or night, weather permitting. I appreciated their unselfishness and total dedication.

* * *

I am grateful to the NWT (some of which is now Nunavut), for all it has given to me. I am a far better person for having lived there. I am blessed to have seen parts of the country most Canadians can only dream of. I had nursing opportunities that I never imagined would be available. Having had the privilege of living with the Inuit, I have the utmost respect for the peoples of Canada's mysterious and wonderful North. As I write this, I am working out of Whitehorse, in the beautiful Yukon, as a northern flight nurse.

My two greatest friends in life are my grown children, Jordan, 25 and Danielle, 24. I raised them as a single parent in Calgary from the time they were one and two years old. They were, and are, my most treasured possessions. Since my years in the North had been such a time of learning for me, I invited both of them to come and experience life here for themselves — but only if they thought they had what it took to endure. I would put up with no criticism of the North or its people. Warning them of the cold and the hardship, I definitely did not paint a pretty picture.

Both of my children came to Yellowknife, perhaps out of curiosity, or maybe just out of sheer naiveté. They have remained residents over the past four years and I doubt they will ever leave the North. When they go south for a visit, they cannot wait to return home. For all the life lessons we try to teach our children, having the opportunity to help mine experience the North is the best teaching tool I could provide. Jordan and Danielle are hearty, tough human beings. I believe that it is because they have survived the North. They have found out what is important in life and are better human beings for it. Material possessions are not what life is about; that was the main lesson I tried to provide for them in Calgary. I have come full circle, being a mother first, and then a nurse. I have endured and discovered what is important in life. What a gift! I owe it all to the North and its people.

* * *

As I conclude these memoirs of northern nursing in Canada's high Arctic, I must give my thanks to the Inuit people of the Kitikmeot and Keewatin regions of what is now Nunavut. The experience of living with these fine people, enjoying their customs and culture, has enriched my life immensely and changed me forever. The memories that I have shared are some of my fondest, as well as some of my saddest. The strength and courage of the Inuit is an enigma to me: their heartbreak, as well as their joy, is unparalleled in any other group of people I have encountered.

Dana Hawes graduated from Mount Royal College in Calgary. She began working in the North in 1994. She obtained her Occupational Health Certificate and her Critical Care Nursing Certificate. She completed all the courses required by the Canadian Aeronautical Transport Systems for work as a flight nurse. Dana presently works at Foothills Hospital in Calgary.

TOPS AND MARTHA: LEGENDS OF THE NORTH

Rick Tremblay BA, BPHE (Hon.)

This story is about the outstanding nursing team of Martha Aldrich and Tops Van Fleet. These are my views, as I understood them at the time. I may have been told how this team was formed, but my memory is unclear about how a Maritimer and a Dutch nurse came to work together.

Starting in Moose Factory, Ontario, their duties were performed in many northern communities in the large version of the NWT. I think they worked in every Medical Services zone of the time: Baffin, Keewatin, Mackenzie (which included the Central Arctic) and Inuvik. Coppermine (now Kugluktuk) is one of the communities where they spent considerable time and where I met them in the 1970s. The community may have had 400-500 people. Martha, being exact, would be able to tell you precisely the length of time and the correct numbers. They were original members of the Northwest Territories Registered Nurses Association.

Martha and Tops were hired together and they worked together in the nursing stations. They were compassionate and caring in their handling of trauma and serious medical problems, as well as the other general clinics such as well baby, prenatal, postnatal and immunization, as outlined by the Medical Services' guidelines. Martha was in charge of the public health work in the school, while Tops dealt with the public health work in the community. Both were midwives and they shared the deliveries. When they went on holidays, they went out together on exotic trips, which meant that they needed to be replaced at the same time. (Martha still does such trips.)

They became an integral part of the communities they lived in, and they were accepted for who they were. They ran a well-ordered operation and adapted to the population around them. (They were unique in their time, given how nursing stations usually functioned.) They did not always follow the strict rules that Ottawa bureaucrats had laid out for them. An example of their forward thinking and adaptation was that clinics were never held in the morning. Because most of the people did not rise until noon, clinics began after lunch. This was contrary to Health and Welfare Canada's directives that insisted that nurses only work 9 to 5. (Yah! Right!) Another practice of theirs that was contrary to Ottawa guidelines was opening up the public health teaching area for other uses, such as the ladies' sewing circle, youth club meetings and community presentations.

Aware of Tops' and Martha's passion for cross-country skiing in winter and hiking in the summer, the community understood that, when they were off doing either of these activities, only a dire emergency would be considered reason enough to call them back to the station. The people realized that being "on call" 24 hours a day had to have certain compensating outlets. They recognized that skiing and hiking were important for these two women, but they also respected their commitment to their jobs.

Soapstone carvings were scattered around on every available flat surface within their living space. I was never able to determine if the vast collection was a result of purchases from the carvers or donations of thanks to the women for services rendered. My suspicion has been that more than half were tokens of appreciation for care given.

Tops and Martha also had to act as hoteliers because there were few places to stay in town, only Red Pederson's A-Frames, which were quite often full, or out of commission. Travelling professional staff, i.e. the EHO, the dentist, doctors, other specialists and myself (the regional nursing officer) would stay in the extra room in the nursing station. Some of these people, I might add, expected to be waited on by the nursing team. Well, Tops and Martha were quick to let you know that they were *not* hotel staff. This did not sit well with many visitors, who either could not or would not take care of themselves.

Whenever I was to stay there, I always checked before leaving to see what fresh vegetables they would like me to bring, and what kinds of meals they wanted me to prepare for them. During the day, I would be working with the community health representative and the health committee. We would talk health promotion over long, late suppers that I would have ready for them when their work in the clinic was done. Mutual respect for, and an understanding of, what these women had to live with, day in and day out, went a long way to forming friendships and collegial support.

On one occasion, two visiting "tourists," Mike Hewitt (who was the zone nursing officer) and I, wanted to stay up all night to record the midnight sun as it approached the horizon, but never set. We used still, time-exposure photography and got some great pictures. The women had pity on us and took turns bringing us warm drinks as the night progressed. They really did not have to do that. They should have been sleeping.

Martha and Tops set up a good system, which met the needs of the people and still allowed time off for themselves. When they left the community, the people went out of their way to show their appreciation. There are many people in Kugluktuk today who still remember them, and many were young adults who were delivered by them.

Sadly, the team was broken up when a freak accident occurred when they were hiking in Ayuittuq National Park in Baffin and Tops died. Martha retired to Nova Scotia where she lived for a few years before moving to New Brunswick where she is now closer to relatives.

Many people didn't even know Tops' and Martha's last names. They only knew who they were and how well regarded they were by the communities in which they worked. These women left a lasting impression on those of us who were fortunate enough to know and work with them.

Rick Tremblay received his BA in 1968 and his BPHE (Hon.) in 1969 from the University of Windsor, Ontario. From 1972 to 1976, he was a health educator for the Mackenzie Zone, Department of National Health and Welfare. Over the years, he worked tirelessly with the communities to promote healthy public policy. He recruited, trained and supported community health representatives in the Dene communities and worked with local health committees in the Inuit communities. He provided inservice education sessions for the nurses in the health centres. Until his untimely death in July 2001, Rick was a consultant for health promotion in the NWT.

MY INTRODUCTION TO INUIT COMMUNICATIONS

Barb Round RN, OHN

When I arrived in Yellowknife in the early 1980s, I was already an experienced obstetrical nurse, but I was completely unfamiliar with the North, northern people and their customs. My first night shift at the old Stanton hospital made me clearly aware of this.

A quiet night was just what I needed to settle into a new hospital and its routines, with plenty of time to read protocols and check supply cupboards. My only patient in the labour rooms was an Inuit woman who was in premature labour. She was over 40 years old, and this was her fifth or sixth pregnancy. The medication was up and running when I arrived, and the woman was not contracting. Throughout the shift, I would dutifully check for contractions, and each time I was unable to detect any.

Our conversations were limited: she spoke Inuktitut and all I could offer was English and imperfect French. We communicated with smiles and nods. After palpating for contractions, I would ask her if she were feeling any contractions or pain. I asked her in English, and mimed with clenched hands over my belly and contorted facial expressions. Each time she responded by screwing up her face. If I checked again, the response was invariably the same. I maintained the medication running in through the IV, and fetal heart and all other indicators were normal.

All night long we repeated this pantomime and in the morning the medication was still running when I gave my report. I noted that, although I had been unable to palpate any contractions, the patient seemed to indicate ongoing discomfort. My first night shift was over.

On my way out, I stopped in to see my patient and said good-bye. When the Inuktitut interpreter arrived for her dayshift, she went in to visit the patient, whom she knew. I asked her to double-check how the woman was feeling. I explained to her that every time I did "this" (demonstrating my pained, hand-clenching contraction pantomime), she would respond with a similar face. I assumed that she was still feeling contractions, even though I was unable to feel any. Translator and patient then had an animated discussion in Inuktitut, with lots of giggles.

The interpreter explained to me the Inuit way of expressing "yes" and "no" through simple facial expressions: raising of the eyebrows means "yes," and wrinkling of the nose means "no." This lady had been signalling me emphatic "no's" every time I had asked about ongoing contractions, but I had been reading the signals all wrong. We had a good laugh about my northern inexperience.

From that day forward, when I gave orientation sessions to all new staff, one of the first things I explained was Inuit facial signalling.

LESSONS LEARNED: CUSTOM ADOPTION

When I was head nurse on Obstetrics at the old Stanton Hospital in Yellowknife, a premature baby was born in our hospital. He was medivac'd to Edmonton, where he was treated in the intensive care nursery, and was returned to us when he was a month old.

The baby lived in our nursery for several months, as he needed to put on weight before he could go home. Because he had a number of medical problems, he required ongoing medication and a special formula. He was a beautiful baby: he cuddled, played and gave big smiles. He was far more interactive than the newborns and we became attached to him. Since his mom was at home caring for her other children in her remote community, I called frequently to update her on the baby's progress.

Eventually, the baby was judged to be healthy and large enough to go home. His mother came down for a few days to become familiar with his routines and to learn how to administer his medication. I prepared the nursing station in the home community for his arrival. I sent information about his special formula and medications, so the nurses there could follow his progress when he got back. When he left, many of the nurses had tears in their eyes.

Two days later, I called the nursing station to check on the baby's progress. The nurses there had no idea what I was talking about. They said the mother had gotten off the plane without the baby and they had assumed he had to stay a little longer in Yellowknife. My phone call set off a panic reaction, and a flurry of activity followed, as we tried to find out exactly what had happened to the baby.

When the dust finally settled, we were told that, while on the plane, the mother had been seated beside a lady from a neighbouring village. The lady was childless and admired the new baby. She confided that she had been trying to adopt. The mother offered the lady her baby, which she joyfully accepted. As soon as the plane landed, she got off with the baby, showed him to her husband, got back on the plane and handed him over to his new adoptive mother. It never occurred to her to inform the nursing station. She had just gone on with her life.

We then had to play catch-up. The nurses retrieved all the extra formula, which had come off the plane with the mother and forwarded it to the next community, along with the baby's necessary medication. The nurses there had to locate the baby. It didn't take long to find the new family. The nurses educated the new mother about the special needs of her baby.

Fortunately, he suffered no ill effects without his prescriptions. The last I heard, the baby was doing very well.

This episode taught me many valuable lessons. For one thing, I became familiar with the practice of "custom adoption," which worked well for the Inuit for many years prior to the arrival of government types with paperwork and legalities. Babies were shared for many reasons: to keep a grandparent from being lonely, to help a young mother who couldn't cope with another mouth to feed, or to fulfill a need in a family without children. This was all arranged simply between consenting parties: a common and well-accepted practice. Custom-adopted children usually grew up with full knowledge of their birth families and often visited back and forth.

I also learned the importance of translation. Even though a patient nods and complies with instruction, translation is necessary to ensure complete understanding of the message. In the case of the baby, the importance of the special medication and formula was obviously not well understood by the mother.

Finally, I learned to "let go" and to try not to judge. This mother did not abandon her baby. She gave him to a loving home. She had other little ones to care for, and had not yet formed a relationship with him in the way she had with her older children. He had been born prematurely and whisked away to receive medical care. He had lived separately from her for months. Seeing an opportunity to provide a safe and caring home for her baby, and with the consent of her husband, she made the best arrangement she could.

It was good that I made that follow-up phone call.

A HITCHHIKER'S GUIDE TO THE NWT

Many years ago, I represented the Department of Health at a ceremony in a remote Sahtu community. I travelled on a plane, chartered by the Commissioner of the NWT, filled with other departmental representatives and family members. The pilot made a brief speech before takeoff, indicating that the plane would be leaving the following day at 10 a.m. sharp. No announcements would be made. There would be no visits to round up stragglers and no waiting for latecomers. Upon landing, he reminded us of this again.

The two nurses at the station, where I was to stay, greeted me warmly. After the ceremony and community feast, we stayed up late into the night trading nursing stories. The next morning we rose about nine o'clock and they insisted on making a huge brunch: eggs, pancakes, bacon – the works. I protested that I would not make my plane; but they persisted and explained that all the planes "buzzed" the town before landing. They assured me that there would be plenty of time for them to drive me to the airport. Meanwhile, the chartered plane had gone to Inuvik overnight and would be coming back for the 10 a.m. pickup.

As ten o'clock got closer, I became nervous. The nurses humoured me and called their friend, the air traffic person in Inuvik, who said that the plane had not yet taken off from Inuvik, and there was no need to worry. We feasted on the lovely breakfast. More than an hour and several phone calls later, we still had not heard the plane. According to Mr. Air Traffic, it hadn't even left Inuvik yet. Shortly after eleven, we heard a plane – loud, overhead and *leaving* the community. A quick call to our traffic man confirmed the worst! That *was* my plane. The pilot had not filed a flight plan in Inuvik before leaving. He had not buzzed the town on arrival (he was not one of the "regulars"), and he had just called in his flight plan for Yellowknife after leaving the community, where I was now stranded.

I was very upset, to say the least. The Commissioner's office had provided me with free travel, and I suspected that my supervisor would not be pleased to pay a one-way ticket home (nor was it high on my personal wish list). The nurses, feeling responsible, promised to find a solution for me. After many phone calls and calling-in of favours, they arranged for me to get a lift home in a cargo plane that was coming in to drop things off at the store that afternoon.

At the appointed hour, the nurses escorted me to the dock where we helped to unload boxes for the store, and then I got in for the ride home. Because the Twin Otter had been converted for cargo, there were no passenger seats, which meant that I had to sit on the bare metal floor, hanging on to a couple of cargo straps. Climbing and banking are far more exciting when you are sitting on a slippery floor, with no supports, than when you are strapped into a seat.

The plane had one more stop to make at a lodge on Great Bear Lake. I was able to get out and have a quick tour of the surrounding area while the pilots and lodge staff unloaded. It was a beautiful place, one I would never have seen otherwise. I arrived home after dinner, tired but happy with my great adventure.

* * *

Once, when I worked in health promotion, I had planned a special trip into a small community, specifically to work with one woman in particular. The plane flew in on Tuesday and came out on Thursday, and I arranged to spend all of the intervening time with her. I had prepared a two-day training agenda. However, shortly after I arrived, my protégé informed me that she was leaving on Wednesday morning for an important committee meeting in the regional centre. She had forgotten to tell me in advance. Since the sole purpose of my trip was to work with her, I offered to go out on the same plane with her, rather than stay in the community with nothing to do. She said that she was going out on a small charter sent especially for her and other committee members from the next community. There would be no room for hitchhikers.

I wandered around the community, looking for something useful to do. Did the school need a speaker? Could the daycare staff use a quick review of health issues? No one wanted me so I faced a long day and a half until my scheduled flight out. Eventually, I dropped by the hotel and noticed a stranger drinking coffee. This was odd. He was not from the community, yet he had not stayed at the hotel the night before. How had he arrived?

As it turned out, the stranger was the pilot of a cargo plane, who was sent in to relocate a household of furniture. He was waiting while the others loaded the truck. A little begging was all that was necessary for me to obtain a seat on the flight. Later that day, I flew out directly to Yellowknife, in a fraction of the time it had taken me to get to the community on a scheduled flight, with connections along the way. My husband was quite surprised to receive a message to pick me up a day early, at a cargo airline hanger.

* * *

As a nurse, I think about my relationship with planes and I recall my first medivac in 1981, which involved moving a pregnant woman in premature labour from Yellowknife to Edmonton. Rather than hire a charter plane, we were put onto the scheduled jet flight. We took up eight seats (four rows) with the stretcher, and temporary curtains around us. (Talk about feeling scrutiny while working!) Privacy for the patient was just about non-existent. Well-wishers poked their heads through the curtains and I could barely hear anything with the fetalscope over the roar of the engines. The good news is that both mother and baby survived nicely.

I also recall a medivac of an elderly woman from Coppermine in 1984 or 85. I had been in town presenting family life education training courses. I was not there officially in a nursing role. The woman, who had severe chronic obstructive lung disease, needed reassessment of her medications, and there were no nurses available to take her out. It was not a difficult job — just basically to escort her, to make sure her oxygen tubing didn't get kinked, and to see her safely to the hospital in Yellowknife.

The memorable part of the trip was getting her onto the plane. The patient was heavy, frail, and confined to a wheelchair. While she was able to walk a few steps with assistance, she could not manage the stairs. The portable ramp at the community airport was too narrow to allow anyone to carry her up. The patient in her wheelchair, with me standing behind her, was placed on a pallet: the kind building supplies come on — an ordinary wooden pallet with slats of wood over a rough frame. I put the wheelchair brakes on, but they weren't reliable.

A forklift raised us both high in the air, up towards the cargo door of the plane. There I was, standing on a shaky, slatted platform, trying desperately to hang on to the wheelchair so it wouldn't fall off the pallet, and terrified of falling off. What made matters worse was the fact that it was windy and minus 40 degrees. The forklift jerked and swayed as it went up and the forklift driver repositioned the machine to aim us at the plane.

What followed was a bizarre ballet. Once we were at the right height, a group of us tried to manoeuver the wheelchair off the pallet and into the plane. With the wheelchair stored in the cargo section, the patient and I sat in regular seats for an uneventful ride to Yellowknife. At the receiving end, where a wide staircase was available, two men performed a "fireman's carry" to take the woman down the stairs and to her wheelchair.

Planes are a fact of life in the North. Everyone has at least one story about being "weathered in" in a community, being rescheduled, or landing unexpectedly someplace. These particular stories were some of the ones that I will always remember.

Barb Round graduated in 1971 from the Victoria Hospital School of Nursing in London, Ontario. Since 1981, she has lived and worked mostly in Yellowknife. She received her Certificate in Occupational Health from the University of Manitoba in 1996. Barb has travelled the North in a variety of roles including Family Life Education Coordinator and Health Promotion Consultant. In her educational role, she was one of the first to introduce participatory group work in the communities, encouraging recognition and responsibility related to family and community problems. She was Recruitment and Retention Consultant for the Department of Health and Social Services, GNWT in Yellowknife. At present, Barb is Executive Director of the NWT Registered Nurses Association.

FORT McPHERSON, NWT: A COMMUNITY PROFILE

Winnie Greenland, Community Health Representative

Winnie gathered this information to assist the nurses who have come to her Health Centre.

Fort McPherson is a hamlet, situated on the east bank of the Peel River. Lakes and muskeg with stunted forest surround it. Located a few miles to the west, are the Richardson Mountains and the Yukon border. The hamlet is on the Dempster Highway, which joins the city of Whitehorse in the Yukon with Inuvik in the NWT. From May to July we have twenty-four hour daylight and in December, we have darkness for almost twenty-four hours.

Fort McPherson is between two river crossings. In the summer, these crossings are served by two ferries: one across the Peel, eight miles to the west and one across the Mackenzie, to the northwest near Tsiigehtchic (formerly Arctic Red River). During freeze-up and break-up, all road traffic comes to a standstill for up to six weeks. Ice roads are used in the winter to cross the rivers. The airport is about two miles out of town and is operational all year. Sometimes bad weather makes it impossible for the planes to land.

The population of Fort McPherson is approximately a thousand. The majority of us are Gwich'in Indians. We live mainly on native foods due to the high costs of store foods that are brought in from the South. Hunting and trapping are a common way of life for the Gwich'in people. The beading and sewing of home-tanned moose hides, which is done by the women here, is very popular. A few local men do some painting, drawing and carvings. The church to which most residents belong is Anglican, and there is also a Northern Evangelical Missionary preacher residing in the community.

Our drinking water comes from the intake lake, which is 1.8 km from town. Eighteen homes, the school, the RCMP Station and the Health Centre are on the utilidor system. (A utilidor is an above ground water delivery and sewage disposal system.) The water is treated with chlorine and then trucked to the remaining homes. Most people have sewage-holding tanks, which are pumped out regularly, and the sewage is disposed of near the garbage dump.

Garbage is not burned in town anymore. We used to burn it in forty-five gallon barrels. Now we put it into bags, which are placed outside in plywood boxes provided by the hamlet. The garbage is collected about three times a week and then taken to the dump about six miles from town and burned. Every so often, the burned garbage is covered with a layer of broken shale gravel.

A Sergeant and four Constables who enforce the law staff the RCMP detachment. They also have a secretary and twelve people who are on call to guard prisoners. A janitor helps to keep their detachment offices clean.

The Peel River Alcohol Society is well-established with two full time counsellors and a co-ordinator. Counselling is offered on an on-going basis. Social Services, which has two full-time workers, also provides counselling.

The Post Office, which is operated by the Teetl'it Co-op, is open every day to provide us with mail. Mail comes in on Mondays, Wednesdays and Fridays. There are two stores, the Northern Store and the Co-op store. They sell clothing, hardware and groceries. We depend upon them mostly for vegetables and fresh fruit. However, the older people prefer meats and vegetables from the land. We do not have any banks, so we get cash from the stores.

We receive CBC Radio from Inuvik. The community also operates its own station, CBQM. Morning programs are aired by different organizations: school, Social Services, Health Centre, RCMP, Indian Band and Housing Office. The people provide evening programs voluntarily. This is a vital communication link to the many people who live out on the land. Most people have telephones and we can get nineteen cable channels through the Teetl'it Co-op.

Two hundred and twenty students attend the Chief Julius School. There is one principal, a vice-principal, twelve teachers, one special needs teacher, one special needs assistant, three special needs trainees, two native language teachers, one pre-school teacher, one school counsellor and two janitors. Pre-school to grade twelve are taught in the community.

The Gwich'in Language Cultural Centre employs three local women to translate and publish books for school children and others. The Adult Education Centre provides upgrading for adults who want to further their education. The programs are operated under Arctic College.

The Health Centre is a four-nurse station. We have a secretary, a part-time janitor and housekeeper, a community health representative and a dental therapist. Homemakers provide services to the elders and are paid by the Band through a contract with the Department of Health. They also supervise people, especially youths, who are put on probation by the courts.

The NWT Power Corp (formerly NCPC) employs two men. The power plant provides electricity to 98% of the community. The Tent and Canvas Shop employs thirteen people. They sew tents, bags, Ski-Doo covers, teepees and sleigh wrappers. Teetl' it Zheh Trucking employs local men to maintain the highway from the Yukon border to Tsiigehtchic. One Wildlife Officer protects the wildlife by making sure that people hunt only in hunting season and take only the amount of game that is needed. Starting in May, they also employ seven seasonal workers to fight forest fires.

The community of Fort McPherson is staffed by two heavy equipment operators as airport maintainers (clearing runways etc.), one maintainer (or janitor), a receptionist, an administrative clerk, a financial clerk, a senior administrative officer and a by-law officer. They will hire a recreation co-ordinator and a swimming pool supervisor. The Mayor and eight councillors govern the hamlet.

The Housing Office administers and maintains public housing. It employs three permanent maintenance staff, two casuals, one janitor and four office girls. Seven board members control the organization. The Department of Public Works employs three men who maintain the government buildings.

There is a campground about 8.3 miles west of the hamlet, along the Dempster Highway. An Information Centre provides tourists with information about the area. Every summer many tourists from all over the world pass through our community.

The Chief and Councillors control the Teetl'it Gwich'in Band. Gwich'in people had a land claim settled in April, 1993.

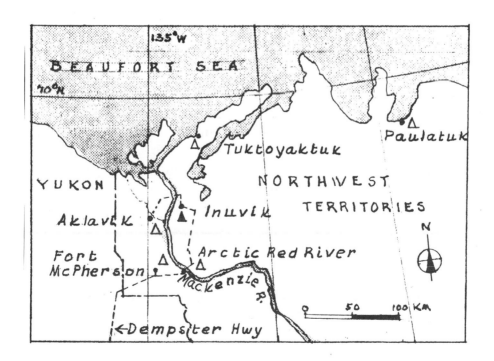

COMMUNITY HEALTH CARE

In April, 1988, the Government of the Northwest Territories took over the delivery of health care from the Federal Government. At that time, the nursing station's name was changed to the William Firth Health Centre. This is a four-nurse station. While there has been a large turnover of nurses, some to replace those on holidays, we are lucky to have a few nurses who will stay for a year.

The old station was erected in 1972 and is an interesting design for a cold climate, with ceiling peaks twenty feet high in both residence and clinic area. It was the last station to have shared accommodations for the nurses. A new building with separate living quarters was completed in January, 1992. The living quarters consist of six apartments, one of which is reserved for short-stay professionals, such as doctors.

We have one community health representative (CHR). Our national organization feels that there should be one CHR for every five hundred people, although a lot of communities have only one CHR. We try to educate and promote health. Weekly radio presentations are the most effective way to get our information to the people. To ensure that diseases are prevented, we also provide sanitation and environmental health checks. We act as a liaison between the community and the health team. It is a job where people count most. We work with the young and old, creating activities for our centre to host. Bringing the community to work as a whole and obtaining good health is our goal.

A doctor comes to the clinic once a month for about three days. Our medical specialists come to us once a year and to Inuvik more frequently. These include an ophthalmologist, an internist, a dermatologist, a gynaecologist, an orthopaedic surgeon, as well as an ear, nose and throat specialist. A dentist comes to the station every three months and stays for about ten days. Preventive dentistry, including dental health education, is given special attention. These services focus on the care of the children. Any patient whom the nurse feels should be hospitalized is reported to the doctor on call at the Inuvik Hospital. They then order medications or organize a medivac. The medivac team comes from Inuvik; the pilots act as stretcher-bearers.

Winnie Greenland was born, raised, and attended school in Fort McPherson, Northwest Territories. In 1983, she began working for the Department of Health as an interpreter at the nursing station. Winnie trained in Inuvik as a Community Health Representative and since 1990, has served Fort McPherson in that capacity. She has seen many, many nurses pass through her health centre.

I NURSE IN A PLANE

Gwen (Peyton) Daly RN

A Nurse is a Nurse…
I disagree.
Nursing is different
In the NWT.

As for me,
I nurse in a plane.
A shift for me
Is never the same.

I nurse in a plane,
Hospital by air,
Transport the patient
And all of our gear.

The plane is small.
Our imagination must do
To recreate Obstetrics
And Intensive Care too.

We answer all calls
Be it day, or by night.
Referral makes arrangements.
We go to the site.

The beeper goes off.
My heart skips a beat.
A lady in labour.
The third one this week!

A lady in labour:
That's a two-nurse call.
Here comes my partner.
She runs down the hall.

Where is the patient?
What plane do we take?
Quick! Get the answers.
We've decisions to make.

One hour – our goal.
Sixty minutes – that's all
To get in the air
From the time of the call.

It's a short little hop
To Lac La Martre.
How fast are the contractions?
When did they start?

To the nurse at the station
We're a sight for sore eyes.
A lady in labour
Is certainly no prize.

The nurse is alone
Or maybe one more.
We do our assessment,
Then head out the door.

Today it's Lac La Martre,
Next time, Lutselk'e?
Could be west to Wrigley
Or north to Spence Bay.

We've transported all ages,
Newborn to ninety-six.
With different diagnoses:
We've had quite the mix.

This job is a challenge.
My teammates are rare.
There's Lona and Joyce
And Nicki and Claire.

Five nurses we are.
We work in a plane.
Nursing for us
Just isn't the same.

A Nurse is a Nurse...
I disagree.
Nursing is different
In the NWT!

Gwen (Peyton) Daly graduated from the St. John's General Hospital School of Nursing in St. John's, Newfoundland in 1981. After a decade of working in Intensive Care, she moved to Yellowknife where she flew with the St. John Ambulance Air Medivac until its demise in 1995. She maintains it was the best job of her life. Gwen now lives and works in Edmonton, Alberta.

THE BLIZZARD TWINS: A RANKIN INLET STORY

Calum Lunn RN, BSc, D of M Sc

Rankin Inlet's blizzards are notorious, especially to those who have lived through them. In the winter of 1997, my wife and I experienced numerous blizzards but the memory of one blizzard, with its dramatic events, left an everlasting impression.

My wife, Elizabeth, and I were both flight nurses for Keewatin Air. In this line of work, one is exposed to many out-of-the-ordinary challenges. In January of 1997, we decided to spend some of our days off working at the Rankin Inlet nursing station, in what is now called Nunavut. Rankin Inlet is 912 miles north of Winnipeg, approximately 289 miles north of the treeline. Usually, we don't spend much time thinking about the treeline. However, you do when it is minus 35°C, and the winds are howling at 90 km an hour. A snowfall magnifies the blindness caused by the drifting surface snow, for there is nothing to stop it.

One evening, we received a telephone call to help out at the nursing station. Neither of us was on call that night so we knew the circumstances had to be unusual. They were. A pregnant woman of 33 weeks gestation had gone into early labour (the normal duration for pregnancy is 40 weeks). To make matters worse, her most recent ultrasound had shown that she was carrying twins. By some strange twist of fate, the nursing station was at its full complement of health-care workers. In total, two physicians, two midwives and four nurse practitioners would eventually attend the delivery. The first challenge would be to get there.

* * *

At 6 p.m. on a regular January night, Rankin Inlet is a beacon on the tundra as its diesel-generated lights illuminate the star-lit landscape. On this particular night, only one light could be seen from our apartment. It was a dim glow even though it was only 30 yards away. This was one of the few times that we wore our full northern outfits: wind-pants and a scarf for Elizabeth, snowmobile pants and a balaclava for me, with gauntlets, Sorels and a Snow Goose parka for each of us. It felt like we were wearing space suits. Our hoods were extended out as far as they could go, but the fierce wind pushed them back as we took our first steps outside.

I had Elizabeth walk in front of me as we headed towards the only visible light. I did this so we wouldn't get separated, but I admit she helped to break the wind for me. If this seems extreme, you should know that every year in Nunavut people die from getting lost or turning the wrong way in a blizzard, even though they are in their own community. We continued from light to light along one of Rankin's main roads. When the visibility is this poor, you do not have to worry that a snowmobile or a car might hit you. We were lucky that this was the town's best-lit street. Thirty minutes later, we reached the nursing station, tired, but with only the small exposed areas on our faces feeling cold.

Elizabeth and I were the last ones to arrive at the hospital. The full team met in the reception area to discuss the case. The patient had been in labour for only two hours and was just three centimetres dilated (10 cm is fully dilated). This gave us a bit of time to prepare. While infants born at 26 weeks can survive, extreme measures might have to be undertaken.

At 33 weeks, the twins would have a low supply of glucose (the sugar needed to fuel a whole host of the body's chemical reactions). They would also have a small fat supply, which would make them vulnerable to heat loss. Lastly, the infants would have an immature immune system. This would leave them susceptible to infection, especially respiratory infection, since immature lung tissue has a tendency to collapse, thus trapping microorganisms and allowing them to grow. With infants of this age, pneumonia and sepsis (an infection which can cause microorganisms to grow and spread in the circulatory system) can be life threatening. To reduce the risk of these complications, it was agreed that an intravenous would be started in each infant and glucose would be administered. This route would be used to provide two types of antibiotics, both known to protect against a wide variety of microorganisms. A decision was made to borrow a second incubator from Keewatin Air so that each infant could be kept warm, at a temperature close to the environment it had been swimming in for the last eight months.

Our concerns were also extended to the mother. The risk of uterine bleeding after delivery was on everyone's mind. Although Rankin Inlet Nursing Station kept a supply of packed red blood cells, it only maintained a stock of two units (approximately 500 ml). The rationale was that it was only needed to start a blood transfusion to allow for time to medivac to a hospital where more blood could be given. This small supply would be grossly inadequate if our patient had a large bleed or even a small continuous bleed, since the weather would make evacuation impossible.

* * *

It was also standard procedure to set up all available resuscitation equipment in order to plan for a worst-case scenario. A second set could be borrowed from Keewatin Air. The problem was that the equipment was stored at the airport, approximately a mile away. I phoned the dispatcher who selected the aircraft engineer, Craig Mackie, who would brave the blizzard to collect me and drive me to the airport.

Twenty minutes later, he arrived. He told us that the road he had driven on had drifts up to a foot high and that he had experienced numerous whiteouts. At times, he had had to stop until he was able to determine where the road was. I returned to my "spacesuit" and joined Craig in the half-ton truck. Fortunately, it had 4-wheel drive, which we needed, since the road was slick and the drifts were packed hard. About 100 yards from the nursing station, we experienced a whiteout. Although we were only going about 20 miles an hour, we were both thrown firmly against our seat belts as we came to a sudden stop. I knew that we hadn't hit a house or another vehicle because there was no crashing sound, but I was unsure about what we had struck. When the whiteout cleared to a soupy haze, we saw that we were up to the axles in a snowdrift. Craig attempted rocking the truck back and forth while I vainly tried pushing.

Unfortunately, there was no shovel in the truck and we decided that I should return to the nursing station to get one. Again, I headed towards the only visible light. Once I was about 30 feet past it, I had one of those sensations that are impossible to describe. A whiteout started, and the world went black. I could only freeze my position. As the haze began to thin, I realized that I didn't know exactly where I was. I decided that I would go a few paces forward, and if I couldn't figure out my position, I would quickly turn and follow my footsteps back to the truck before they were swept away.

As soon as I spied the CO-OP store, I knew that the nursing station was only about 75 yards away. A few houses along the way partially sheltered my path. After what seemed like 20 minutes, I returned to about 20 feet from the truck, only to see Craig rock it out of its position and head back towards the nursing station. I had a few choice thoughts for him as I trudged back, shovel in hand, but I remembered that he had been dragged out of his warm, comfortable home to help us out.

When I reached the station, Craig greeted me at the door and we agreed that it was pointless to attempt the journey without a snowmobile. As luck would have it, the patient's husband overheard us. He had a Ski-Doo and would be more than happy to give one of us a lift to the airport. We decided that it made more sense for Craig to go so that I could help in the preparations for the delivery. For the record, if I could have predicted the upcoming events, I would probably never have asked the husband for his assistance.

Approximately an hour later, Craig and the husband returned with the incubator and the resuscitation equipment. The husband had dark brown areas of frostbite, which covered each cheek and his forearms where his gloves and jacket didn't quite meet. Apparently, about three-quarters of the way to the airport, they had hit an unseen snowdrift and were sent flying off the snowmobile. Luckily, they both hit the ground together because, as Craig told me later, he had become disoriented when he landed and couldn't see the snowmobile. Once the whiteout passed, the husband followed the tracks back to his runaway machine and restarted it. They continued, but had to stop about 30 yards away because of a large drift. After making their way through waist-deep snow, they reached the hangar. We were glad to hear that their return journey was less adventurous.

* * *

During their absence, the medical team had already set up the delivery room in case the twins arrived sooner than expected. This involved warming up the receiving table (where infants are first laid after being born) as well as the incubator, testing the suction equipment and attaching appropriately sized suction tubes. Oxygen equipment was prepared and tested, and all of the resuscitation equipment was laid out and tested.

Meanwhile, they prepared the mother by inserting two large needles in order to start intravenous lines with normal saline (a liquid which is used not only to maintain fluid in the circulatory system, but also when blood has to be transfused). She was informed of the possible procedures so that she would have no surprises. She was a calm woman who listened well to the breathing instructions given by the midwives and followed them to the letter.

Duties were divided up among the medical team based on who had the most experience in a designated area. All we could do now was wait patiently while the labour progressed with the coaching of the two midwives. At this point, I would like to emphasize to those who have never been involved in a delivery, that the mother is truly the one who does most of the work in labour. Much attention is focused on the medical and nursing personnel who are in attendance and who are now given much of the credit for a delivery. In reality, it is the mother who endures the pain and effort of birthing.

We did not have to wait long. After three hours of labour, the physician repeated the pelvic exam to assess the dilatation of the cervix and found it to be 10cm, or fully dilated. All members of the team were called into the room where they assumed their set roles. By now the incubator and the receiving table were warm. The room was also kept warm to reduce the shock of the temperature change that would be experienced by the twins. The mother was encouraged to push with each contraction, and each time she did, a tiny head came closer and closer. After about 10 minutes, the first baby's head was guided out by the physician's hand. The mother was asked to stop pushing and to pant.

Elizabeth passed a sterile suction catheter to the physician and gentle suction was applied as it was passed first into the baby's mouth and then into each nostril. As this was being done, I turned on the oxygen to my bag-valve mask (the device used to ventilate the infant). The mother was asked to give one more push, which freed the infant's anterior shoulder, and then a small, totally gray infant girl emerged. Her umbilical cord was quickly clamped in two places and cut by the physician.

The baby girl was placed in the hollow of my forearm. She took up only half its length. I quickly placed her on a warm blanket on the receiving table. An infant has to be dried quickly to minimize heat loss and to reduce the need to burn precious calories to keep warm. This done, I threw the blanket behind the table and immediately applied the mask over the infant's mouth and nose, and attempted to squeeze a breath in. The chest remained motionless. I repositioned the mask and tried another breath. Again, nothing. The nurse in front of me realized that my position at the infant's feet might be the reason I could not get a good seal on the mask around her face. She asked if she could give it a try, as she was at the baby's head.

I immediately traded the bag-valve mask for the suction catheter. On the nurse's first attempt, the baby's chest rose, but only a quarter of the way. The second ventilation brought it no further. Without a word, she removed the mask and I suctioned fairly deeply into the throat. A moderate amount of clear fluid was removed. Again, the bag-valve mask was placed and this time its chest rose fully. The nurse continued her ventilation at the rapid rate required for newborns. Now the other physician moved closer with his stethoscope to listen for the baby's heartbeat. "100," he said. This is a very slow rate for a newborn. If it remained this slow, chest compressions and medications would have to be given. The other nurse and I looked at each other, both knowing that the next word from the physician would mean we would either continue what we were doing, or drop the equipment and grab the resuscitation tray.

We had previously gone over drug dosages, and I now tried to estimate the baby's weight to know which of our calculations we should use. The physician was hunched over, listening intently. Finally, "120" was heard. A collective sigh was heard. While 120 is still too slow, it showed that the heartbeat was improving, and that oxygen would be circulating as needed, and, most importantly, that the resuscitation tray would remain where it was. While waiting for the next heartbeat report, I glanced over to see Elizabeth carrying the second infant over to the incubator. This distraction lasted only momentarily, since I knew that we weren't yet out of the woods with this baby.

Reassurance came with each heartbeat report and finally a smile came to my face as I heard a cry. It started off as more of a gurgle than a cry, but then developed into a beautiful loud-pitched scream. About two minutes had passed since the delivery and the baby's morbid gray skin tone was turning into a beautiful pink. The other nurse and I had changed positions and I continued to supplement each breath with a little puff of oxygen. As the baby's colour kept improving and she showed her ability to breathe, I gradually removed the mask and placed the free flowing oxygen near her nose.

My nursing partner for baby number one had worked in pediatrics for many years and was the logical choice to start the intravenous. Everything had been prepared: tapes were ripped and arm-boards made out of tongue depressors. A newborn tends to show her veins since her fat reserves are so small. Still they seem no bigger than a hair fiber and the challenge is to enter the vein without going right through it. While I continued to monitor the breathing and administer oxygen, I used my free hand to hold down our little girl's legs. The physician did a great job of immobilizing the elbow. This is difficult since an infant finds an incredible number of ways to twist and turn. What made matters worse was that, even though she had been dried recently, she was covered, as premature newborns often are, with vernix caseosa. This is a cheese-like substance, which has the same consistency and texture as axle grease.

The other nurse prepared herself, taking one last look to make sure that all the tapes and the primed intravenous line were within reach. An alcohol swab was used to clean the area and to remove the vernix, which tends to build up at the joints. While the physician continued holding the elbow, she laid the needle beside the vein and slowly advanced the point under the skin. Ordinarily you would see a small drop of blood in the plastic bulb attached to the needle. However, in cases like this, the blood pressure is so weak and the blood vessel so small, that you can only tell if you are in the vein by feeling a pop as the needle punctures the vein. The nurse was on her own, as any movement by the physician or me would dislodge the needle. She slowly advanced the fine catheter over the needle into the vein. Almost immediately, we knew she was in: the telltale darkening of the clear plastic tubing verified the accurate positioning of the needle.

The tourniquet was removed and the intravenous line attached. The slow drops of blood along the intravenous line were the final proof we needed that the catheter was in the right place. A mass of bandages was used to immobilize the taped intravenous line within the arm-board and the intravenous line was placed into a pump. Finally the blood glucose was checked. Premature infants have a small supply of glucose in reserve and a poor ability to control their glucose levels. A tiny needle prick to the heel was needed to get the one drop we required. Our little one had a blood glucose level of 5.2 mmol/litre, well within the normal of 4 to 7 mmol/litre.

No further interventions were required. We closely monitored her temperature, her breathing and the intravenous line, as well as assessing the amount of oxygen in her blood using an oxymeter. The fact that our baby girl was stable for the moment gave the physician and the nurse with whom I had been working a chance to help out with the other infant. Elizabeth later informed me that the delivery of her baby had gone more smoothly. No assisted ventilations were required, and our resident expert in pediatric lines had started the next intravenous.

* * *

Our next challenge came when we checked the mother. The placenta, which normally is delivered 10 to 15 minutes after the child, had not released from the uterus. The obstetrical physician had applied gentle traction but to no avail. This was not good. If there was partial separation of the placenta, there could be a large amount of blood loss that would be hard to control, since the drugs usually administered would cause the uterus to clamp down.

The physician phoned a specialist in Winnipeg in order to determine the best course of action. Usually, a procedure calling for the manual removal of the placenta is required at this stage. However, we had a few extenuating circumstances. Manual removal is ordinarily only carried out when there is a large supply of blood and an available operating theatre for the surgery that may be needed. And we had neither of these. In consultation with the doctor in Winnipeg, it was decided to leave the placenta in place and to cut the umbilical cord as short as possible to minimize its exposure to infectious microorganisms. As an added precaution, we would give the mother antibiotics. The two large bore IV lines would be left in place in case of bleeding.

Once these procedures were carried out, the general atmosphere of the room changed from tension to exhaustion. The blizzard continued to rage and showed no signs of letting up. Shifts were established to divide up the time needed to look after our three patients and also to attend to the other emergency patients who had braved the weather. Elizabeth and I were given the chance to go home to have dinner and get some sleep in preparation for the night shift. We would care for the three patients, while a third nurse would look after the outpatients and relieve us for breaks. The station doesn't stop because we have a delivery in progress.

* * *

Walking home was less of a chore since we knew that we would get some rest. With the wind in our backs and the slippery roads, the journey was more of a sailing adventure than walking. You only had to raise your arms and you were off, sliding down the street. The problem was trying to keep your balance. I was glad for the dark and the poor visibility so that no one mistook us for having had one drink too many.

The warmth of the apartment was welcoming. Dinner was small and quick since sleep was our priority. Earlier in the week, I had awoken and drawn back the living room curtains and I had seen a *komatik* (a large Inuit sled) with a man on it, being pulled across the frozen inlet by a team of eight dogs. I had paused and smiled then, realizing that I was privileged to see a way of life which was unchanged – even with all the southern influences. This memory was now far from my thoughts. The idea that we would have to fight the wind again when we returned for a 12-hour night shift (with only three hours of sleep) was uppermost in my mind.

One a.m. came quickly as Elizabeth and I blew in through the front doors of the nursing station. We learned that the condition of the patients was unchanged. Their blood sugar levels remained within the normal range. The fact that the oxygen saturation was within normal limits was a good guide for when the twins had to be suctioned for the mucous that clogged their airways. Their intravenous pumps continued to infuse well, and full physicals had revealed no abnormalities. The mother's temperature remained normal and she showed no signs of bleeding. Everything looked good. Elizabeth and I took our positions next to the infants, knowing that we were in for a long night.

* * *

As the night progressed, we learned the life story of the mother, a pleasant Inuit woman. Elizabeth assumed the primary care of the mother and the stronger baby. Most neonatal nurses will tell you that a premature girl will do better than a premature boy of the same weight. But in our case, the girl was smaller and frailer. To her credit, she was a cutie. Some infants are bruised, or have their heads shaped so oddly by the birth canal that they are nicknamed "conehead." This baby girl had a beautiful, but small, round head. She looked even cuter as someone had made her a toque out of stockingette, which gave her an elf-like appearance. A facecloth was rolled up to prop her over to one side to allow any fluids to drain from her mouth. A flap of a towel shielded her eyes from the bright light above the receiving table that also provided warmth. A diaper was placed under her but not fastened at the front since it would block the heat from reaching her.

The intravenous was running well. Because the attached oxymeter consistently registered normal values, the oxygen had been discontinued. Nevertheless, the suction equipment and resuscitation equipment were kept close at hand. Most of the night was spent with Elizabeth and me trying to stay awake by discussing our wedding plans for Ireland. Our plans were interrupted by the routine duties of antibiotic administration to each of our three patients, replacing syringes of fluid and staring at the little chests to assess the depth and character of the respirations.

The less routine events were the suctioning of each infant for the tiny amounts of mucous, which dropped the oxymeter readings. This caused minor variations to the rise and fall of each chest and caused larger variations to the caregivers. The other challenge was to restart the IV to each of the infants.

* * *

As the end of our shift neared, we became aware that the winds were calming. The morning light allowed us to see the buildings across the street. Visibility improved. Word cannot describe the joy of being relieved after a tiring night shift. This morning was no exception, as we anticipated a warm bed and sleep.

Later that day, we learned that our twins had been bundled up into a single incubator to be transported with their mother to the hospital in Yellowknife. There had been a break in the weather and the window of time to transport them was brief. A phone call came from the flight services station to say that this would be the only break. The two-day blizzard was turning into four, and the drop in winds would only be short lived. The patients were rushed out to the airport by ambulance. The backlog of patients who had been housebound over the last two days eventually thinned, and the exhausted caregivers began to see a light at the end of the tunnel.

* * *

I don't know the statistical likelihood for this situation to occur again, so soon, and at the same nursing station. But another woman who went into labour and gave birth also experienced a retained placenta. This delivery (not twins this time) seemed easy compared to the first one. Maybe we had the routine down pat. There is nothing like working on autopilot.

At the end of the blizzard, the medivac plane from Keewatin Air was able to land in Rankin Inlet and I was able to resume my regular flight-nursing job. The infant and the mother with a retained placenta stabilized and it was decided that I would go with them to Winnipeg. It felt great to get back to my home on the airplane, a King Air with a medically dedicated interior. I was looking forward to catching up on some sleep.

* * *

This story ends on a happy note. Two years later, I flew into Rankin Inlet to pick up a two month-old child with bronchiolitis (an infection of the airways). As usual, there was a group of patients in the waiting room and family members of people involved with my medivac. I introduced myself to the mother of the patient and gave her a brief overview of what I would be doing on the flight to Churchill, Manitoba. She smiled and asked, "Do you remember them?" In front of me were two active little tots running over the seats with wet boots. (I had medivac'd close to 700 patients in the north, so many remained a blur.) Her smile turned to my smile as I realized that these two little ones were the twins of our blizzard adventure. What a rare thank-you!

Calum Lunn graduated from the University of Winnipeg in 1982 with a BSc in Chemistry and Biology. He studied medicine at the University of St. Andrews in Scotland and graduated in 1984 with a Diploma in Medical Science, with merit in Medical Microbiology. He graduated from the Grace Hospital School of Nursing in 1989. In 1994, he became a flight nurse with Keewatin Air. He was stationed in Churchill, Manitoba for four years and for one year in Rankin Inlet, Nunavut where he met his wife Elizabeth. They were married at the Cabra Castle in Kingscourt, Ireland in 1997. In 1999, he transferred to Critical Care International, an organization based in Winnipeg, which transports patients worldwide.

MEMORIES MADE 'NEATH THE MIDNIGHT SUN

Jan Stirling RN, BscN

During the many years that I have spent nursing in the North, I have had many unforgettable experiences. Here are but a few of my recollections.

In 1971, just after I had arrived in Yellowknife where I had been hired as a public health nurse, I had to go on a medivac to Bay Chimo. It was a cold and windy Labour Day weekend. Having never been in a single Otter before and not realizing there wasn't a toilet on the plane, I drank coffee. We landed on floats in high winds with snow flurries. We were surrounded by cliffs and there were no trees. Waiting for us when we arrived, were five adults and three children, none of whom spoke English. My main concern was the patient at hand, but I also needed to find a place to go to the bathroom. The Inuit, realizing my predicament, directed me to a little shed with a pail. Then I went to see the patient, a 21-year-old man who was sick with a ruptured appendix. It had taken them two days to paddle to Bathurst Inlet to access a radiophone to report that this man was ill and to ask for help to medivac him out. In those days, even the stations did not have a telephone system. I assessed him, gave him Demerol for pain, put up an IV and brought him back to Yellowknife. He had surgery immediately and survived.

One Christmas Eve, I had a medivac to Gjoa Haven for a newborn with some problems. The infant was in the incubator, and the mom, the dad and their two-year-old came along. All of us sat around the baby and looked after it. I remember the pilot turning around and commenting, "This isn't your typical biblical scene, but it reminds me of the birth of Christ."

I recall the time I delivered a baby in a plane over Great Slave Lake on Easter Sunday. That was quite an experience. We started off with the pilot, the patient and me, and we returned with four people. This family still lives in Yellowknife, and I often see them.

Another time, I flew in to Rae Lakes for a man who had cut all his fingers to the bone while chopping wood. At that time, Rae Lakes did not have many permanent buildings. This man was in a tent frame with an airtight stove going full force. Everyone had crowded in to see what I would do. It was so hot it must have been 90 degrees. I gave the patient emergency treatment and got him into the back seat of the little Cessna. The priest requested permission to come out to Yellowknife with us. I agreed and he got into the front seat. Just as we were going to leave, a trapper ran up to us and asked, "Nurse, will you take my furs to the fur office?" He stuck this big pile of furs, which were still dripping, in behind my head. As soon as we started moving, the priest lit up his smelly pipe (there is no smoking on planes now – thank goodness). The patient, half-asleep, fell on top of me, while the furs dripped behind me. When we arrived in Yellowknife, the injured man was taken to the operating room and his fingers were saved.

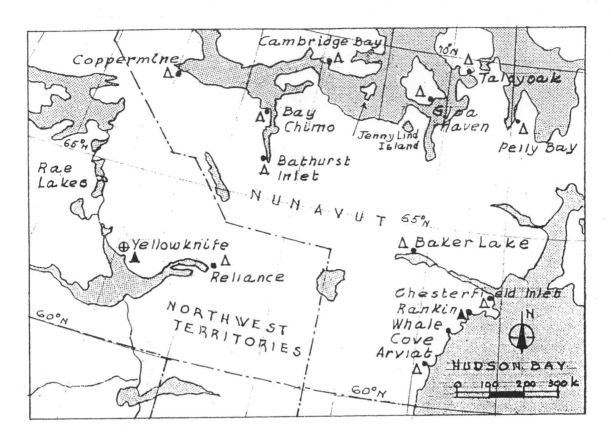

I recall a time when we landed in a small settlement to pick up an Inuit mom who was coming to Yellowknife to have her baby. Her mother was standing beside her, smiling at her and patting me (she couldn't speak English, only Inuktitut). The daughter explained, "My mother is so pleased I'm going out to have my baby because she had twelve children, and I'm the only child left." Years ago, many children living on the land died of pneumonia or other infections, and many died at birth.

On one memorable trip to Fort Reliance, we had to take a small plane in the middle of the night for a mother in labour. There was a snowstorm, and with the diminished visibility and depth perception, we bounced three times before we actually landed. I got off the plane, jumped on the back of a snowmobile with a fellow I had never met before and drove for miles. All of a sudden I thought, "What am I doing? Where am I going?" At the radio station, they had a mom who had come in out of the bush. The woman was in labour and she had been chopping wood. A block of wood had hit her face, causing her jaw to swell. Besides that, she was nauseated. The big decision was whether to fly her back in the storm or to let her have the baby in the radio station. I gave her something for pain, which slowed down the labour. Finally, we were able to take off, and the woman had her baby in Yellowknife.

I'll never forget another medivac when I was gone for 16 hours. We had to fly to Cambridge Bay, where the weather had already closed in. We had to stop at Baker Lake to refuel and then fly on to Pelly Bay, where the weather was bad. Getting a critically ill patient back to Yellowknife, after all those hours of delay, was scary.

During another medivac to Cambridge Bay, we couldn't land because of the weather. We circled around and around, until I heard the air control advise, "You'll have to go to Coppermine." (This community is now named Kugluktuk.) My tension rose when I heard the pilot say, "We haven't enough fuel to go to Coppermine." So we headed for the DEW Line at Jenny Lynn Island, where we had to stay for 24 hours until the weather cleared. During a medivac to Edmonton, our small plane was hit by lightning, and on one trip in to Fort Reliance, there were so many caribou that we had to fly around and around, trying to scare them away before we could land. It is no wonder that my family was always worried when I was away on these long trips.

* * *

A number of years ago, we did relief work in the nursing stations, which I always enjoyed. The nurses in the field worked on-call 24 hours a day, never knowing what they would have to cope with. The first night I was in Coppermine to relieve, I told the staff, who had been going night and day with a croup epidemic, that I would do any callouts. On this particularly cold September day, I had visited Bloody Falls on the Coppermine River with the Anglican minister. At the falls, we had noticed some Inuit men going off to hunt with bows and arrows. That night, when I was in the nursing station, the alarm bell went, which meant someone needed help. I looked at the door and had a fright. I didn't know what was standing there. In front of me was someone (a werewolf, I wondered?) wrapped in caribou hide, with the belly fur on his head dripping blood down his face.

It turned out that the fellow had shot a caribou with a bow and arrow, and when the caribou had tried to escape with the arrow, he had chased it. While doing this, the man had thrown off his jacket and lost it. He and the others had returned to their boat with two or three caribou to skin, but no jacket. Since the weather had turned cold and windy, he had used the skins to keep warm. When this man arrived at the station, he had hypothermia so severe I couldn't get a temperature at all. With the help of his wife and a friend, I was able to get him into a bathtub and we gradually heated up the water. In a few hours, he warmed up and was fine.

These are a few of my "memories made 'neath the midnight sun." I have loved all my years working in the North, in this incredible land, with its wonderful people.

Jan Stirling graduated with an RN from St. John General Hospital in New Brunswick and with a BScN from the University of Ottawa. She has lived all over Canada, as well as in Japan and Germany and has nursed in many of these locations. During the Korean War, she served as an Armed Forces Nursing Sister. Since 1971, she has worked in the Northwest Territories, and was nurse-in-charge of the Yellowknife Health Centre for twenty-five years, a position she retired from in October, 1997. Jan still lives in Yellowknife. She is involved in many health issues as a member of a number of committees, including the Yellowknife Health and Social Services Board.

FORTY YEARS OF NORTHERN NURSING

Sister Cecile Montpetit GNM, CM, RN, BSc, PHN, NP

On receiving my Grey Nun assignment for the northern missions in 1955, I accepted it with some apprehension, yet with joy and readiness. Ready I was, but reality soon sank in. Transportation and travelling in 1955 was overland by rail, a long and interesting trip as far as Edmonton, Alberta. Then a rumbling train ride took me to Waterways, Alberta and to the end of the rails. How does one reach Fort McMurray? "Try the best you can." A truck proved to be an interesting means of transportation, but better than walking ten miles.

At St. Gabriel's Hospital in McMurray, I was given a short assignment, and that was the beginning of a long career. On arrival, I found a small hospital staffed entirely by fellow sisters. The night nurse being sick, I replaced her. My personal belongings, however, were still in Edmonton! The nursing sisters were quick to provide me with a supply of borrowed white aprons.

One day I had to face a difficult situation in the doctor's absence. A woman arrived at the hospital very pale and extremely weak. Her complaint dated back to the birth of her four-month-old baby who had been born in the bush. I suspected haemorrhaging. All we had in the laboratory was a hemoglobinometer: a little tube used to compare her blood with the normal colour of blood. It was obvious that she desperately needed blood. So, I prepared for at least three pints of fresh blood.

As she received them, she progressively regained energy, but there was a reaction at the beginning of the third bottle. The blood transfusion was discontinued while I searched in my "nursing bible," the Merck Manual, to find what was a proper dose of epinephrine. Did I give her an extra drop of the powerful medication? I did not know, but for a few minutes her heart was pumping much too fast. Finally, the reaction was controlled, her heart was beating regularly, the patient was grateful, and I was the one in shock.

Three months later, I pursued my journey north to St. Ann's Hospital in Fort Smith, Northwest Territories. Night services were to be my new duties. Although I found working in this hospital very different from my training days in Quebec, I was happy to be on night duty. It gave me time to get better acquainted with the various types of patients: medical, obstetrical and pediatric on the first floor, and tuberculosis patients on the second: 80 patients in all. St. Ann's Hospital, founded in 1914, served a population of about 3000. There was one doctor, and if he had surgical credentials, it meant he would operate. Needless to say, the sisters of my community were very happy to welcome me from Montreal. The greetings were gratifying, but I had to study English in earnest. That was a priority.

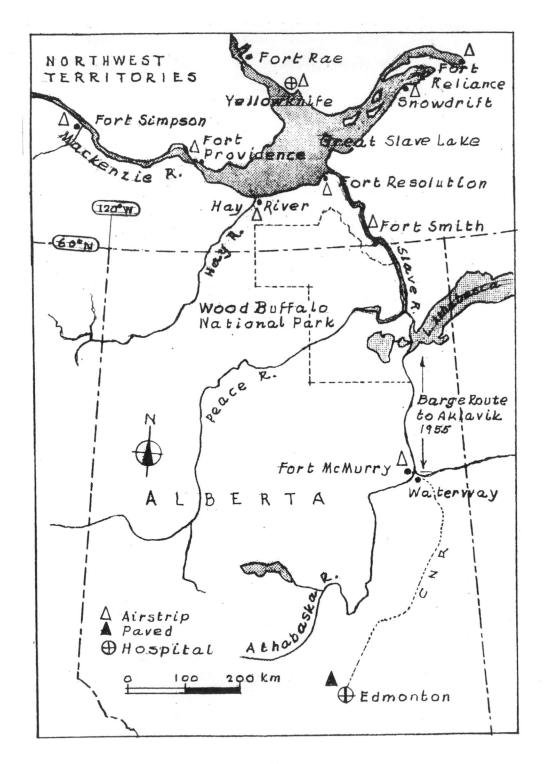

The North American Indian culture started to mean something to me. Reading on this subject was a necessity. I also continued with my nursing duties. Gradually, I was exposed to many new people and new working tasks such as laboratory work, radiology, admitting procedures and training of new personnel. After seven years of intensive work: twelve hour shifts, seven days a week without leaving town (there was no road), except for three weeks allowed annually, and locally, for an eight-day retreat and a semblance of holidays, I was granted leave to go east and visit my family in Montreal.

* * *

Upon my return, I was transferred to Fort Resolution on the south shore of Great Slave Lake, NWT. It was a small hospital with TB in-patients and a doctor who visited regularly. I was appointed nurse-in-charge. The duties included organizing nursing services for outpatients as well as for inpatients. I also set up the administrative and business office. Always ready to face every medical situation that would arise, I sometimes had to do dental work, because there was no dentist, and no access road.

I remember one particular day when many different things happened. In the morning, a crying mother arrived at the hospital holding a bundle of clothes. Lo and behold, her beautiful six-month-old baby was dead (a crib death). After attempting to console the devastated mother, I became the undertaker. I prepared the baby and placed him in a tiny coffin made by the family. No sooner was this task completed than Old Sam pleaded with me to sew his dog's abdomen. It had been wounded by an axe. After lunch that day, I delivered Violet's fifth child. (A month later, on a sunny winter day, grateful Old Sam offered me a dog-team sled ride. The lead dog was none other than my "ex-patient.") Thus, all knowledge acquired was very useful.

After further training in Ottawa (1967-1969), I went back to Fort Smith as a public health nurse. This shift from institutional nursing to public health nursing was easy for me, because I was convinced that health promotion was important. Keeping people healthy was better than nursing them back to health from a problem that could have been avoided. The medical situation in northern hospitals, except for Yellowknife and Inuvik, was simple: one resident doctor. Preventative health care occupied the best part of my working days, in the homes and at the school. Immunization programs were important to avoid epidemics. Providing chronic care to the elderly and following up on tuberculosis patients were ongoing activities. Pre-natal care was always a busy section, along with child care at home. Education of the native people was carried out by dispensing knowledge using leaflets, videocassettes, and consultations.

Medical consultations with specialists were done by phone or radio transmitter. When a patient needed special care, he was generally transferred to a multi-diagnostic centre. A regularly scheduled plane was used whenever possible. In remote areas, with only a small landing strip or water access, a small plane would be called in to transfer the patient — and always with a registered nurse escort. That, too, was part of my job description. Getting into those single-engine planes with a stretcher case, and flying at low altitude, right into a headwind, was no fun. Very often the plane's temperature was freezing cold. The bush pilot flew with his own "eye radar" and visibility was not always 100%. In the early days, I was airsick most of the time. Then, the nurse was ailing more than the patient. Frequently, the landing was bumpy; but one always welcomed the feeling of being "down to earth." Thank God, after a long while, I overcame airsickness.

The patient was then either admitted to one of the local hospitals or transferred to a larger centre on a regularly scheduled flight. In an emergency, a charter would be requested. After 1970, twin-engine airplanes were in greater use in the North, to the delight of the nursing team. They were more spacious for stretcher cases and much safer. Weather is always an important factor in flying; sometimes trips were delayed from one hour to two or three days because of it. In critical situations, a forced landing would sometimes occur, much to my anxiety.

* * *

As time went by, a health care program was organized in the high Arctic. Nurses from the South took bravely to the challenge. However, nurses who went on sick leave or holidays, or who resigned, were not replaced immediately. I would then be asked to substitute in various nursing stations, and for longer periods, in the high Arctic and around Great Slave Lake. It was an adventurous and pleasant experience. I learned about the Inuit culture, the local people, and the white people above the 65th parallel, as far north as Gjoa Haven. While English was the language generally spoken in business and health matters, in the distant Forts and with older people, I had to acquire a vocabulary of more than 60 words in different dialects. Of course, a few laughs were in order; but the people were charming and ever ready to help me.

When they worked in institutional hospitals, the Grey Nuns lived together in an organized way of life, which we called "community life." We met for lunch, for prayer, for socializing in the evening, and for festive occasions. They were rewarding, healthy moments. There was time also for hilarious ones. We had a common purpose, a definite goal: to reach out to the native population in every possible way. As a public health nurse, hired by the federal government, I lived alone in federal living quarters, far from a Grey Nun community. During this time, I remained in contact with my fellow Grey Nuns. I remember an Inuit housekeeper who couldn't figure out why I tidied my room every morning. She wondered why I opened my curtains even if it were pitch dark outside, until one o'clock in the afternoon, with twilight the rest of the short day. No doubt, she thought I was expecting the sun to shine soon.

The federal government, faithful to its practice of continuing education, offered to send me to a nurse practitioner course given at the University of Alberta in Edmonton. As well as building the nurses' own self-assurance in delivering their duties, the program was designed to train nurses who work in outpost settings to make more accurate diagnoses, so as to prescribe appropriate medication and treatment.

* * *

I was stationed twice in Fort Rae, NWT for a total of 14 years. At the Rae Health Centre, I soon began the proper prevention activities. Pregnant women appreciated pre-natal classes. Likewise, initiating home care for tuberculosis patients and chronic cases was a new approach that was well received. Families willingly and fully co-operated.

I once had a patient suffering from meningitis who had to be evacuated to Charles Camsell Hospital in Edmonton. Of course, the airways would not accept the little boy on the airplane. Danger! I waited five hours at the airport by the patient's side until he was accepted on the last carrier heading south. They would not soon forget me.

Transportation of patients to the Stanton Hospital in Yellowknife from Rae became a major problem. The construction of an incessantly winding road was even a blessing. Fort Rae township acquired the first ambulance. I planned the set-up of the vehicle and initiated the young personnel responsible for its maintenance, as well as the drivers. The ambulance attendants were given special attention because of their importance on the team. Their training included first aid, triage, CPR (cardiac pulmonary resuscitation), carrying severely injured patients, and making sure up-to-date medication was always available in the ambulance.

Local women gradually became more involved in all health services. They attended Aurora College, either in Yellowknife or in Inuvik, NWT and obtained certificates as community health representatives. They were very proud of their achievement. Some pursued their study of x-ray techniques to be able to detect and follow up the resolution of tuberculosis. Their chest x-rays were the best. The CPR certificate was also awarded on graduation day. For some graduates, it was their first diploma. They are the most valuable helpers we have, because they assure permanence and direct communication, without translators.

Record-keeping at the health centre in Rae-Edzo was extensive. Staff co-operation was a requisite. The computer age was welcomed because there were five communities to keep records for: Rae Lakes, Lac La Martre, Snare Lakes, Edzo and, of course Rae, a population of about 2000. Speaking of numbers, I think I can say that during my nursing career, I delivered over a thousand babies. I remember one death, but there are three sets of twins and one set of triplets who are very much alive.

* * *

As I look back on those forty-some years, there are two thoughts that I would like to share. Alone, I would not have been able to carry on with the workload. The Good Lord was definitely on my side, along with my guardian angel. My second thought is for all the local people who gave me their confidence and trust, and who co-operated with me, eager to help their own people. It was my pleasure to work with them. My sole disappointment is that there is not yet a native RN ready to take charge. On leaving, I was overwhelmed, and deeply touched, by all the testimonies of gratitude and of appreciation that I received. These years of my life I shall never forget.

Sister Cecile Montpetit graduated from Ecole des Infirmières at Hôpital Saint-Jean in Saint Jean, Québec in 1954. In 1969, she obtained her BSc PHN from the University of Ottawa. Presently retired, she does part-time nursing in the Grey Nun's Motherhouse Infirmary in Montréal. In 1990, Sr. Montpetit received the Order of Canada. The text of the investiture reads as follows:

> *For 35 years this member of the congregation of the Grey Nuns of Montreal has worked as a Public Health Nurse in the isolated regions of the MacKenzie River in the Northwest Territories. She has humbly dedicated herself to serving others and has enriched the lives of the citizens of her northern community, reflecting the devotion the Grey Nuns have demonstrated for this region for over a century.*

In 1992, Sister also received recognition from The Venerable Order of the Hospital of Saint John in Jerusalem. His Excellency, the Honourable Ramon Hnatyshyn, then Governor General of Canada, sanctioned, on behalf of Her Majesty, the Queen of Canada, her promotion to the rank of *Sister Servant of the Order of Saint John.*

A SPECIAL LUNCH

Marilyn Brownlee RN (EC), BScN, CCOH, FNP/C (US)

In September, 1980, I was recruited to work in outpost nursing in Sioux Lookout Zone. As part of my orientation to "bush nursing" at the Zone Hospital in Sioux, Rose Pogoda presented me with a pig's foot to practise my suturing techniques. I departed Sioux Lookout via Austin Airways, with my pig's foot in tow, for my first posting in the fly-in community of Pikangikum. Upon my arrival at the nursing station, I stowed my precious pig's foot wrapped in butcher's paper in the refrigerator. On the outside of this package, I had written in big letters, "DO NOT TOUCH.".

At the Pikangikum Nursing Station, the nurses had the benefit of a live-in housekeeper-cook. A few weeks after I arrived, the physician, Lillian Wong, made a visit to Pik. After a hectic clinic morning while she was there, the nurses and the doctor sat down for lunch. Our cook seemed particularly pleased with herself that day because of what she had prepared for us. I was late arriving for the lunch that consisted of homemade soup and bannock.

I proceeded to ladle the soup from the pot and, much to my horror, I saw bits and pieces of black thread floating on top of this greenish-gray coloured soup. I wondered where it had come from, when suddenly it hit me. It was suture material – and my pig's foot was missing from the refrigerator! This soup had been concocted from my now well-aged pig's foot. I was horrified. All I could think of was that we were all doomed to die of food poisoning from this decaying animal foot. I gestured to the doctor not to eat any more. She was on her second bowl at that time.

We roared with laughter afterwards, since we all lived to tell the tale of our pig's foot soup.

Marilyn Brownlee graduated from the University of Saskatchewan with a BScN in 1979. She obtained her NP from the University of Alberta in 1982, a CCOH (Occupational Health) in 1988, and an RN(EC) in 1999. In 2000, she received her Certification FNP/C (US). Marilyn worked for 22 years with the Medical Services Branch, her last position being an occupational health nurse in Southern Ontario Zone. She is presently the Clinical Nurse Practitioner at Central Park Lodge in Toronto, part of a pilot project for the Ontario Ministry of Health.

A RECIPE FOR OUR MEDIVAC TEAM

Lona (Schick) Heinzig RN, Claire Madill RN, Nicki (Bayfield) Ash RN, Joyce de Ruiter RN, Gwen (Peyton) Daly RN, all members of The St. John Ambulance Air Medivac Team, Yellowknife, NWT, 1993

Preparation:

- Line a 500,000 square mile pan with a map of the Northwest Territories, paying specific attention to the Mackenzie Region.
- Take five Registered Nurses from across the country and place in Yellowknife (most flavourful when combining as many provinces as possible).
- Blend in several years of critical care experience.
- Make sure to include *generous* amounts of the following: common sense, endurance, a caring attitude, adaptability, independence, self-motivation, a sense of adventure, a sense of humour, patience, the strength of an ant (i.e. able to lift ten times your body weight). Add to this, a *dash of insanity.*
- Coat bottom and sides of the pan with the above mixture and begin immediate preparation of the base.

Base:

These steps can be completed in any order, but try to accomplish as quickly as possible.

Note: to ensure consistency, no substitutions should be made

- Updated certification in Advanced Cardiac Life Support, Basic Trauma Life Support, Pediatric Advanced Life Support, Neonatal Resuscitation
- Winter Wilderness Survival
- Advanced Airway Management
- Advanced Obstetrical Management
- Introduction to Aircraft 101 (includes aircraft types, airstrips, weather, etc.)
- Wonders of Aerodynamics 202 (see Hypoxia for You and How Gas Expands at Altitude)
- Foreign Policies 303 (Discover the complexities involved in air medical transport... it's not just "throwing patients in a plane" and flying.)

Press firmly into the prepared pan.

Filling:

Meanwhile, for every flight, combine the following:

- Begin with a thorough telephone patient report obtained from the nurse at the health centre. Anticipate from this the need for special interventions prior to departure. Critical interventions include special medications, blood, a second nurse or a physician, or an RCMP officer.
- Mix the basic transport equipment including oxygen, suction, survival gear, flight bag, medication box, IV bags, pulse oxymeter, stretcher. Further additions will depend on findings in Step 1 (i.e. IV pump, cardiac monitor, OBS or trauma kit, etc.).

Regardless of how quickly you move, be prepared to "Hurry-Up-And-Wait"... for the taxi, the fuelman, the pilots, the weather, etc.

Gradually stir in:

- The ability to work in small places with big boots, parkas, gloves, long underwear, hat, scarf and windpants.
- The development of a sixth sense to compensate for the noise, vibration, darkness and cold aircraft environment.
- The ability to survive for days on end with only coffee, chocolate bars and peanuts. (Ask yourself: "What is Canada's Food Guide?")

Variations:

Any flight may be subject to folding in the following:

- You may need to sit and wait for an obstetrical patient to deliver in the health centre. (Babies do not like to make their debut in cold, cramped airplanes.)
- Additional patients may be added during flight, or you may be re-routed. Be prepared.
- Helicopter calls come up occasionally and are generally stress-inducing.
- On occasion, no planes are available: innovation is a _must_ at times like this.

Pour entire mixture into the prepared pan.

Topping:

Sprinkle evenly with the available patient transportation method.

Variations:

- Komatik (a sled pulled by skidoo)
- Open pick-up truck (If possible include a tailgate...that opens *and* closes.)
- Suburban/van (Make sure seats are removed to accommodate stretcher.)
- Ambulance (preferred...whenever available)

Transport Tip: When the thermometer dips below zero (Celsius), watch for frozen IVs and oxygen bottles. (This is to be avoided at all cost.)

Bake at temperatures ranging from +30° to −30° Celsius. Do not forget to include the windchill, blizzards, fog, or in the summer months... the mosquitoes.

At frequent intervals, test (with a toothpick) for comradeship, energy and enthusiasm, and you'll have the makings of a dedicated *northern* critical care medivac team. *Creativity* is a *must*...there is no end to the variations that add flavour to this *unique* recipe.

NORTHERN NURSING OBSERVATIONS

Joanne Smith RN, BScN, PHCNP

This article is dedicated to the memory of Louise Stacy, a long time MSB nurse who passed away in October 1998. Louise was my nurse-in-charge for seven years, my mentor and most of all, my friend.

In 1983, I was recently separated and living in southwestern Ontario, having just received my BScN, post diploma. A friend who worked for the Income Security Branch of Health and Welfare Canada kept telling me about "marvelous" nursing positions with the Medical Services Branch in places like Tuktoyaktuk. I declined his suggestions until the day he called to say there were jobs available all across Canada, working with First Nations and Inuit. I applied for a job and was offered one in Clyde River, NWT, half way up Baffin Island. The zone nursing officer who called assured me there would be another nurse and "a doctor every six weeks." This seemed a little too remote for someone new to this sort of nursing. In the meantime, I moved to Fort St. John, B.C. Shortly after I arrived there, however, I received a call from MSB in Edmonton, offering me a choice of three First Nations communities (reserves) in northern Alberta. I decided to be interviewed for the Jean D'Or Prairie position on a Cree reserve of 550 people, give or take a few.

The interview was arranged for early October, only to be postponed a week because the Chief had gone moose hunting. This was my first clue that I was entering a whole new culture. The government flew me to Edmonton and then chartered me, along with the interview board, to Jean D'Or. I had dressed appropriately, or so I thought, in a skirt, blazer and heels. I stepped off the plane onto a grass and dirt airstrip shortly after a rain only to have my heels sink! Now I understood why the others on the plane were casually dressed in slacks and stout walking shoes. I was interviewed by MSB, the Chief and a Band councillor. I found out that this was a one-nurse station with a satellite community. Once a week I would fly to Garden River, just inside the western boundary of Wood Buffalo National Park, and hold a clinic there. The rest of the time, Garden River's health needs would be met by a community health representative who would call me for advice. I was offered the position that day and accepted it.

When I returned to Fort St. John, my significant other and I started to pack. The government had arranged to fly me back to Edmonton and on up to High Level, Alberta, where I was to catch a charter flight to Fox Lake for orientation. That should have been simple enough; however, at that time Edmonton had two airports, and I arrived at the International, but was to leave from the Municipal. Then, because my taxi got caught in traffic, I missed my flight. The next day I flew north to High Level where I was delayed yet again and had to stay overnight, as it would have been too dark to land at an unlit airstrip.

Early the next morning, I received a phone call from the pilot at the charter company that was to fly me to Fox Lake. He said, "Hi. My name is John and I'm flying you to Fox this morning, except it won't be this morning because it's foggy in Fox and we can't land. I'll call you when we're going." I began to wonder if I was really supposed to have this job or if someone was trying to tell me something. I settled in my room to wait. Less than half an hour later, he called back to say they needed a medivac in Fox Lake so we were going after all. We flew in at very low altitude – it seemed like treetops plus fifty feet! Fortunately, having grown up around small airplanes, I was not afraid. We landed safely and the patient was quickly transported to hospital. That pilot, I should add, has remained a good friend for seventeen years.

After spending a week on orientation in Fox Lake, I was to fly back to Edmonton for an additional two weeks at the Charles Camsell Hospital. On the day that I was booked to leave, just before my plane was to arrive, an unconscious twelve-year-old, who had been sniffing gasoline, was brought to the nursing station. I was to escort him to hospital. In order to get the patient and the stretcher into the Cessna 185, the seats had to be removed, which meant that I had to sit on the mailbags that were also going out to Fort Vermilion.

* * *

I survived all this and settled into a busy life as the only nurse for two communities that were thirty-five minutes apart by air. Garden River, the satellite community, was a beautiful little settlement (not a reserve because it is inside a national park) nestled among the evergreens on the north shore of the Peace River. At that time, there was only one phone in town, a pay phone on a telephone pole in the middle of the community. If my CHR needed a medivac, she had to go to the telephone pole and call me collect and I would organize the flight. Someone had to stay by the pole so that I could phone back with the ETA of the plane. This often was a very frustrating experience for everyone. Shortly before I left, in 1989, there was a telephone in every home, something the rest of the country had taken for granted for many years.

Lighting the airstrip for a night landing was also a new experience for me. We dipped rolls of toilet paper in diesel fuel, placed them in tobacco cans, and then set them on fire so the pilots could see the landing strip in the dark. It worked very well. After several years, the government provided portable runway lights that we set out along the sides of the runway; but the pilots preferred the toilet paper ones because they showed up better.

One evening when my husband and I were relaxing at home in Jean D'Or, a young lad came running up to our door and asked us please to come quickly because his brother had shot himself. We grabbed our emergency supplies and took off in the government Suburban which was all we had for an ambulance. While we were driving down the road, the boy suddenly told us that the car that had just passed us had his brother in it. We immediately turned around and headed back to the health centre. As we jumped out of the vehicle, expecting to find a badly

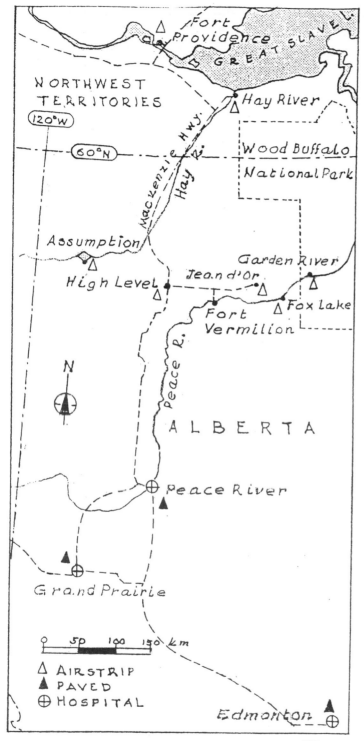

NORTHWEST TERRITORIES

120°W

60°N

Fort Providence

GREAT SLAVE L.

Hay River

Mackenzie Hwy.

Hay R.

Wood Buffalo National Park

Assumption

High Level

Garden River

Jean d'Or

Fort Vermilion

Fox Lake

Peace R.

ALBERTA

N

Peace River

Grand Prairie

0 50 100 150 km

△ AIRSTRIP
▲ PAVED
⊕ HOSPITAL

Edmonton

wounded man, we saw the brother get out of his car with no shoe on one foot. There was a bandaid on the top of this foot and another on the bottom! Apparently, he had been drinking and he decided to clean his rifle. Looking down the barrel, he had seen something move and shot it, only to realize it was his foot. An x-ray revealed he had done considerable damage, having broken several bones.

About four o'clock one morning, a man appeared with his wife at our door, telling us she was "sick." I soon learned that this was their way of saying that she was in labour. On examination, I discovered that the woman was fully dilated and ready to deliver. I had already called for a plane, but there was no time for it to reach us before the baby would arrive. The mother had not had any prenatal care, as she had always eluded us whenever we had tried to get her in to see the doctor. She was forty years old and overweight. According to the dates she gave us, the baby was at least a month early. Soon after her arrival at the centre, she delivered. The baby, which should have been premature, and therefore small, was at least eight pounds. Shortly after birth, the baby went into respiratory distress. About that time, I received a phone call from the flight control centre who informed me that the plane had turned back due to icing of the wings. We would have to wait until first light and get a small plane from Fort Vermilion, rather than the twin engine with the paramedic, which we had expected.

Our health centre did not have an incubator because, I had been told, we were not a nursing station and, therefore, did not do deliveries. My husband ran home, took our three-month-old adopted daughter out of her basket, which he brought to the nursing station, and we lined it with hot water bottles, laid an oxygen mask beside the baby's head, and put a heat lamp above it.

Eventually, the plane arrived and I set off, with the mom on a stretcher and the baby wrapped in blankets in my arms so that I could monitor his breathing. En route, he stopped breathing but I successfully resuscitated him. When we arrived at the hospital, I told the nurse that the doctor was expecting us and asked that she please notify him. But she informed me that he was making rounds and couldn't be disturbed. Again, the baby stopped breathing, and I suggested she might like to call the doctor immediately, or be held responsible for the death of the newborn! She "found" him at once.

I assisted with the care of the baby and at the doctor's request, accompanied him to Peace River to meet the neonatal team that was flying up from Edmonton to get him. With the weather deteriorating, they were afraid they would not be able to land in Fort Vermilion if they flew all the way up. We had ascertained that the baby had very low blood sugar levels because the mother was a gestational diabetic, something we had been unaware of because of her lack of prenatal care. We made the flight safely and transferred the infant over to the team. He lived and did not suffer any long-term effects. Until the day I left the community, that same child would run over to give me a big hug whenever he saw me.

A well-known pediatrician visited our area several times a year, usually bringing an intern with him. On one visit, they stayed overnight with us. The intern was sleeping on our pullout couch in the living room of our trailer. About three o'clock in the morning, I woke up to hear voices in the living room. At first I thought the intern was talking in his sleep. After I listened for a minute, I realized I was hearing Cree, not English. I wakened my husband who went to the living room to investigate. He discovered that a man, whom we had never seen before, had walked into our living room, undressed and crawled into bed with the intern. The intern, thinking it was a friend of ours, was going to let him stay; but the newcomer wouldn't stop talking. My husband quickly sized up the situation, removed the stranger and threw his pants out after him. To this day, we have no idea who this man was. We started locking our door after that.

* * *

Among First Nations' people, it is not uncommon to give a baby to another family. While we were in Jean D'Or, one of my prenatals was dying of breast cancer. The mom, who went into labour at thirty-four weeks, was medivac'd to Edmonton where she gave birth. The baby girl weighed three and a half pounds. She had several health problems, including necrotizing bowel disease and a heart murmur. At six weeks of age, she was transferred to Fort Vermilion Hospital to gain more weight before going home. At two and a half months, the doctor in charge of her care phoned me to say that the baby could go home. She had been ready for several weeks but the mother was too sick to look after her. Besides that, there were already seven other kids at home, the youngest only thirteen months old.

When I met with the family, they confirmed that they were unable to care for her. The extended family did not want to take the responsibility because of her medical problems, and the community members were reluctant to take her because the father had a drinking problem. My husband suggested that we look after her until the family figured out what they wanted to do. That was in October, 1985. When the mother died in January, 1986, her final wish was that we keep the baby. We became her legal guardians and she is still with us: now, a beautiful and healthy sixteen year old.

* * *

When you are the only medical person in the community, you can expect to see not only human patients, but also pets in need of care. Knowing this, it was no surprise that when our neighbour's dog went several rounds with a beaver, I was called to patch up the "victor," Bozo, the dog. He had a six-inch laceration on his chest between his front legs, a deep cut that extended into the muscle. I phoned the vet for his advice on medications and the type of sutures to use. With the help of The Hudson Bay manager and his trainee, and my husband, I managed to stitch up the dog. I put him on antibiotics as recommended by the vet and he recovered completely. Oh yes, the beaver died.

Writing about dogs and Bay managers brings to mind the time our local manager called and requested that we help him with his puppy, Nikki. When we asked what kind of help he needed, he said it was hard to explain and he thought it might be easier if we just came over to his place. We got there to find that the pup had shoved her head through a wheel rim and couldn't get it back out. After several futile attempts to extract her, we sent the Bay manager to the store for a container of margarine, which we applied liberally to the dog's head and were then able to slip her out of the tire. Both wheel rim and dog survived.

* * *

Whenever the plane came in to Jean D'Or with cargo, mail, or passengers for the nursing station, it would "buzz" the station for someone to go down and meet it. That way you only had to meet the planes that were coming in for you. One Saturday morning about nine o'clock, while I was still in bed, the trailer was buzzed. I ignored it since I wasn't expecting anything on the plane. After the second pass over our house, I decided it really was for me. So I jumped out of bed, dressed quickly and drove to the airstrip, only to find the local herd of horses all over the strip, totally ignoring the aircraft. I drove up and down the field several times before they slowly and reluctantly moved far enough to the side to allow the plane to land. The pilot had known that if he buzzed us I would come down and then the horses would be chased off.

After five years, I left Jean D'Or Prairie and relocated to Assumption, a Dene reserve between High Level and Rainbow Lake, also in northern Alberta. Twelve years later, I am still here.

* * *

The social life of a northern nurse is varied, ranging anywhere from a late night snowmobile ride under the northern lights to a formal RCMP regimental, or Red Serge Ball, as it is called. We dine with doctors, lawyers, merchants and Indian Chiefs. We are included in local happenings such as tea dances, weddings and funerals. The local detachment of the RCMP plays a large part in our lives, both professionally and socially. One evening, another nurse and I were sitting in her apartment, when out of the corner of my eye, I saw something move. I turned just in time to see a mouse scurrying across the floor. I screamed and climbed on the back of the chair. Immediately, my friend was up there with me! We decided there was only one course of action to take – we phoned the Mounties. Responding at once, they did a thorough room-to-room search; but the culprit had escaped.

* * *

These are only a few of my experiences over the seventeen years that I have spent in the North. Through my work among the First Nations of Alberta, I have met many wonderful people. I am frequently asked why I stay in remote areas and the answer is simple: I am a nurse practitioner and I love the variety of work. The second question is usually how much longer am I going to stay. My answer? I haven't decided yet.

REGINA'S STORY

Regina Pastion of the Dene Tha Band at Assumption, Alberta is a well-known and respected elder and role model, who has worked for many years in the health field as a community health representative. She has had the unique opportunity of helping to strengthen and support her people as a caregiver. Long before she enrolled in the CHR program at Fort Qu'Appelle in Saskatchewan, she volunteered her time to work with the nurses at the Hay Lakes Nursing Station. In those days, there were no vehicles and home visits were done by walking through the community. When the nurses treated the sick and made general visits to the elders or families, Regina would introduce herself to the people and translate for those who could not understand English.

She was also involved in health education. There were children with impetigo, scabies and head lice, all due to lack of sanitation. At the clinic or in the homes, she often demonstrated to families how they could treat and prevent disease from spreading from one family member to another. Most of the houses had no toilets, only out-houses. Wastewater was often thrown out the door, frequently causing injuries when it formed into ice during the winter. There was a need for healthier living and for an improved standard of living. Regina knew what staying healthy was all about. She had learned these skills when she was at the convent with the nuns. It was there that she had also learned discipline: chores had to be done until they were done right, and at the convent, there was no doubt about that.

In September of 1970, volunteer experience led Regina to further training in the CHR program. When she returned to work, she orientated nurses new to the field and accompanied them on home visits. She helped to educate parents with regard to the importance of immunization and other health issues. In the clinic, she helped as a translator and participated in programs such as prenatal care, taking blood pressures and weights, testing specimens and helping to encourage good nutrition. To help maintain well-being, she supported the nurse by organizing well baby clinics, and by taking the heights and weights of infants.

Regina remembers how the children would scatter whenever the nurses drove in to do home immunizations. You could hear them warning, "The nurse is coming." She said it was really comical to see the children run out the doors, heading for the bushes or down the creek, or sometimes to see little feet sticking out from under a bed. If the house was out in an open area, she managed to give one or two their shots, and the children would yell and cry. The mother would say, "Don't cry. I told you to run. Why didn't you?" The nurse would then sit down and explain to the mother how important it was for their children to get their shots, so that they would not get sick.

Over the years, Regina has been a large part of the history of community health care in Assumption. Following her CHR training in 1970, her career involved her in many health care programs. She has helped the nurses deliver babies by talking to the young mothers. This helped them to relax and made their labour shorter and less painful. Regina would tell them about delivering two of her eleven children, by herself. Something else to note about Regina is that she never forgets the elders: she bathes them, gives them foot care, and a good joint rub.

At one time, Regina was taught to take x-rays, and she recalls how she collected specimens and took x-rays of patients, followed by the TB programme. After developing and drying the films in the dark room, she would label them with the patient's information and mail them to TB services in Edmonton. Sometimes the reports would come back saying the patient was developing TB. Regina also reminisces about the times when she took x-rays of bone fractures and mailed them off to the family doctor. She is sure that she must have done a good job because all the x-rays she took seemed to turn out okay.

As the years have gone by, the health services have changed. While Regina has, in some instances, helped to nurse people in their homes, treatments are no longer done there. Now, people have to come to the nursing station if they are sick. Regina has found that encouraging people to accept such change has not been easy. Teaching people new things is often a long process. For her, learning about holistic health has confirmed her strong belief that people can help heal themselves and stay healthy.

Now 75 years old, and still working as a CHR, Regina Pastion says that she has learned to be patient, and to listen, in order to understand. As a role model, Regina has demonstrated a strong commitment to share her knowledge and improve the health of her community – the community of Assumption, which she has served for the last 35 years. To acknowledge her work, the Dene Tha Band has presented her with an award of community recognition.

Joanne Smith graduated with a BScN from the University of Windsor in Ontario in 1982. She completed her Primary Health Care Nurse Practitioner certification at the University of Western Ontario in London in 1996. She continues to work in Assumption, Alberta.

GO NORTH FOR AN EXPERIENCE LIKE NO OTHER

Heather Thomson RN, BScN

It was on a cold February morning that I left Ottawa, aboard the first of five planes I was to take for my trip to Muskrat Dam. Feeling excited and curious, I tried to absorb every sight and sound. The landscape changed dramatically as the buildings disappeared and were replaced by trees and more trees, while the engines propelled us further north with every turbulent bump of the increasingly smaller planes. For my eight-week consolidation practicum for the University of Ottawa School of Nursing, I was assigned to the Nellie Fiddler Health Centre in Muskrat Dam First Nation, a native community of 250 people in northwestern Ontario. My experiences there would convince me that I was to become a "Nurse of the North."

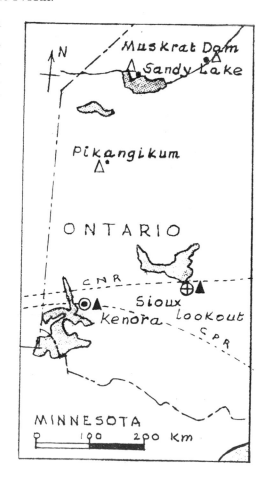

I landed in Muskrat Dam late in the afternoon and was welcomed by my preceptor, Janet Bolger RN, and the health centre staff: health director, referral clerk, community health representative, mental health worker, nutrition educator, driver/janitor and family services worker. The community members greeted me as Muskrat Dam's second nurse. (No, wait…I was still a student nurse; so at best there were 1.5 nurses, a point that would be revisited several times during the next eight weeks.) It quickly became clear that the nurse is important in this remote community because she or he is the entry point to the health care system.

As I interviewed my first patients, I encountered a language barrier, and I began to see how cultural influences affected how I would interact with people. I was face to face with patients who couldn't understand or read the words that I would write, to explain the dose of their medication. Here, people were more verbal, and experiential, learners who were not focused on the written word. Thinking back to the lessons on verbal and non-verbal communication, I explored new ways to listen with my eyes, as well as my ears, and to speak with actions as well as my voice. I, too, had to learn new words in a new language.

Through much practice and study, my clinical skills developed. Every day, community members arrived for clinics for prenatal and well baby checkups, immunizations, hypertension and diabetes follow-up, acute illnesses and general walk-ins. No two days were the same – which was both unsettling and exhilarating. Identifying specific assessment findings (for example, bulging tympanic membrane) helped to build a knowledge base, while the grouping of several assessment findings helped to develop the diagnosis (for example, primary source of infection: ears versus throat). This process evolved over the eight-week period, during which I asked Janet many questions on specific findings and consulted several textbooks.

Having these added responsibilities projected me into an expanded scope of nursing, which was unfamiliar territory to me. Physicians made the diagnosis, or so I had been taught at university. In an isolated community health centre staffed with nurses, it was my role (with supervision) to make the diagnosis, as well as to prescribe treatment and follow up. Of course, there were clinical guidelines to observe, and a physician could be reached by phone for any questions or emergency cases. I struggled with all of this until the end of my practicum, when Janet provided feedback that I did have the necessary assessment and analytical skills to do it. I was turning into the critical thinker that my professors told me I would become.

During my last week in Muskrat Dam, a man in his fifties came to the clinic complaining of chest pain. Janet got on the phone with a physician in Sioux Lookout who interpreted the ECGs that we sent by fax and gave us medication orders to manage the patient's pain. The patient was having an "evolving" myocardial infarction. If his MI (heart attack) "evolved" and his heart stopped, there was no emergency equipment available for him. We managed to keep the patient stable for the six and a half hours it took to get him evacuated by plane to the cardiac care unit in Winnipeg. This emergency clearly illustrated for me the vulnerability of people living in remote northern communities and the dependency of community members on the only health professional typically there: the nurse.

* * *

I was welcomed as a colleague and as member of the health care team, and I worked with the nutrition educator on a "Nutritious Snacks" fact sheet for kindergarten and grade one students. The health centre held two blood pressure clinics for elders in the community, followed by a visit over tea and bannock. Janet and I gave presentations to the First Response Team on multiple trauma and childhood fevers. The nursing process took on a new dimension because the components of assessment, diagnosis, plan, intervention and evaluation were not confined to a single visit with the patient at the health centre. Each encounter, whether in the health centre, at the store, or at a social event, was now included in the development of a therapeutic relationship.

The importance of participation in community activities became clearer as the weeks went by. I joined in many of the community activities: ice fishing, wood chopping, crafts and beading classes, pancake breakfasts, meditation classes for women, birthdays, and feasts, lots of feasts. I acquired quite a taste for moose stew! My participation was facilitated by Janet's friendship and connectedness with the many residents of Muskrat Dam. The highlight of social activities was the Tenth Annual Gospel Jamboree, a four-day festival of music, food and fellowship, during which the population doubled with family and friends visiting from near and far.

Cultural differences had an impact on my behaviour. One day as I was rushing about the health centre (as we city folks do), the community health representative watched quietly. At one point, I paused and began to realize that time holds a different meaning here. No one else was in a rush. The events began when the key people arrived, not at a specific time, which often made keeping an appointment schedule at the health centre a little tricky to manage.

While I was in Muskrat Dam, the word "isolation" took on many meanings for me. It meant limited fresh fruits and vegetables, and fewer nutritious food options. It meant that access to other health care professionals was a phone call away, and that critical patients had to be evacuated by plane, weather permitting. It also meant that appointments for x-rays and ultrasounds necessitated a flight out, and often, an overnight stay in Sioux Lookout, Round Lake or Thunder Bay. Satellite television brought news and programming from across Canada; it was strange to be connected to local events in Ottawa while being so far away. With no high school in Muskrat Dam, older children had go to school in larger communities, and this caused an unnatural break in the family. To maintain my links with family and friends, I sent weekly e-mails that contained excerpts from my journal.

Through these experiences, I gained an insight into the people of Muskrat Dam First Nation: their hardiness, strength, capability and sense of humour. I'll always remember many bright sunny days and starry nights with the northern lights dancing across the sky. Most of all, I remember being welcomed by the people of Muskrat Dam and taking my first steps, from being a student nurse to becoming a graduate nurse. The opportunity to live and work in a community of people who respect each other, who work together to seek solutions to problems, who laugh often and who welcomed an eager, curious, and sometimes funny, nursing student from the South, I will always remember.

I left Muskrat Dam in late March and headed south for Ottawa. It would only be a few months before I would head north again, this time, as an RN.

ATTAWASPISKAT: ONE NURSE'S EXPERIENCES

In August, 2000, I joined the team of eleven RNs working at the Attawapiskat site of the James Bay General Hospital (JBGH), a 16-bed hospital (eight chronic and eight acute) with a clinic for ambulatory and emergency care. Being a fully qualified nurse in Attawapiskat provides a variety of nursing experiences, as well as life experiences.

In my four months here, I've been involved with many emergencies, including overdoses, postpartum hemorrhage, fractured vertebrae, carbon monoxide poisoning, viral meningitis, burns, atrial fibrillation and premature labour. All of these patients were evacuated by helicopter or airplane to hospitals in Moose Factory, Timmins or Kingston for treatment by physicians, specialists and surgeons.

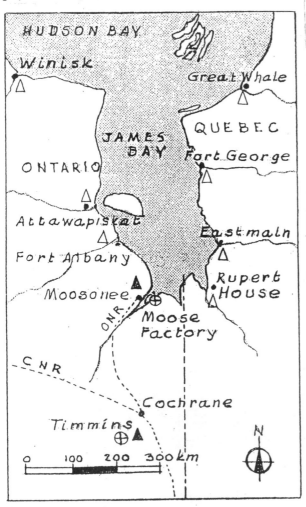

As a team of nurses, our role is to keep the patient stable and ready for transfer. This can be quite challenging, particularly when transfer of the patient is regularly delayed by poor weather. Emergencies often occur in the trauma room, with each nurse taking on different roles. These include starting IVs, monitoring vital and neurological signs, administering medications, getting more information on precipitating and aggravating factors, managing the many family members and friends, and talking by phone to a physician at the Weeneebayko General Hospital in Moose Factory. A situation can be made worse when specific medications are not at hand (e.g. blood products are not available onsite) or when stocks of medications are depleted during the emergency.

The team goes beyond the nurses here to include physicians, physiotherapists, nutrition educators, psychiatrists, ophthalmologists and dentists in Moose Factory, as well as the support of health care aides, children's aid workers and counsellors, community health representatives and teachers in Attawapiskat. The nurse, however, remains the first, and often only, health care professional available to community members. Thus, he or she, must be able to adapt to any situation, and work within a team to navigate the health care system in order to access other health care professionals and services.

Besides emergencies, community members come to the ambulatory clinic for prenatal and postpartum visits, well baby and well women exams. We treat infections on a daily basis. Diabetes and hypertension are regularly followed up, along with treatment of acute illnesses, be they physical or mental. Sometimes these acute patients are admitted into the hospital for observation or further treatment such as IV antibiotics.

In order to operate in such an environment, nurses must be able to perform venipuncture, initiate IVs and administer IV bolus medications; nurses in larger centres also perform these skills. Additional skills performed by nurses at JBGH include suturing, pelvic examination and pap smear, ear and eye irrigation, bivalving and removing casts, incision and drainage of a furuncle, vaginal examination in labour, emergency delivery, neonatal resuscitation and advanced cardiac life support including endotracheal intubation, ECG interpretation, defibrillation and administering life-saving drugs. So far, my skill repertoire includes suturing, pelvic examination and Pap smear, ear and eye irrigation, bivalving and removing casts and vaginal examination in labour. When I put in my first stitches, all I could think about was, "This feels like a chicken!"

* * *

Outside of work, I've had many new experiences since moving to Attawapiskat. First, time flies here – literally. The clocks "speed up" due to inconsistent power frequencies. Each week, I reset my clocks back a half hour. When I first noticed that my watch had a different time from the VCR clock and also a different time from my alarm clock, I thought I was going bonkers! Currently, electricity is produced by a diesel power plant; hydro lines are scheduled to reach Attawapiskat in the spring of 2002.

The water supply for Attawapiskat is generally not potable, as the filtration system does not meet community needs; for example, diesel fuel and coliform bacteria are present on occasion. Potable water for staff is obtained at the hospital or school, and for community members, at the water plant. I've definitely strengthened my bicep muscles, lugging the 18L jug that I fill every week or so. Having to do that, instead of just getting water from the tap in my kitchen, has made me reflect on the problem of environmental contamination and its impact on this community.

I've been learning Cree words so that I'm able to communicate with the elders. Key words are: *wachay* (hello/goodbye), *meegwetch* (thank you), *e'heh* or any affirmative sound (yes), *mona* (no), *tea* (tea), *minnogen* (good), *dakosin* (pain), *ashtom* (come here), *appay* (sit), *bayketch* (slowly) and *dokona* (medicine). I've spelled the words as I've been taught how to pronounce them.

Learning sentences is much harder and I always hope no one is offended at my "broken Cree." I get many smiles each time I try a new word.

Finally, social activities for me include daily walks with several teachers around the perimeter of town (which is eight blocks by eight blocks), hikes into the bush, cheeseburger platters at Kimberly's restaurant on Friday nights, bingos, dances, game nights, holiday celebrations and playing with my cats, George and Steve. I keep in touch with family and friends by regularly sending my "Dispatches from Attawapiskat" by e-mail. As the months go by, I am developing friendships with several community members and am quite comfortable in my new home.

The opportunity to practise nursing in this expanded role is exhilarating and challenging. To live and work with people of a different culture is enriching. To live in a remote community is character building, and to share my experiences is inspiring and motivating. I look forward to many more nursing and life experiences as an RN in Attawapiskat. *Wachay.*

WHAT THE SURVEY SAYS

In December, 2000, an informal, qualitative study was conducted independently by Heather Thomson to explore why nurses choose the North as a practice setting and what keeps them there. A questionnaire was distributed to RNs employed at the James Bay General Hospital in Attawapiskat and the RN employed by Health Canada as a community health nurse in Attawapiskat. The response rate was 58% (7 out of 12). The key themes are outlined in the questions.

Who are the nurses in Attawapiskat?

They range in age from early 20s to 50+ with nursing experience from less than one year to more than 10 years. It is interesting that the nurse's age and years of nursing experiences do not necessarily correlate, as there are some "older" nurses (better to say "nurses with more life experience") who are new nurses. There are 29% male nurses and 71% female nurses. The percentage of nurses educated at college is 43% and of those educated at university is 57%. One nurse is native and has lived in Attawapiskat for many years; the rest come from points south.

Why have nurses come to practise in Attawapiskat?

They look for a variety of nursing experiences and challenges. They seek to work more independently, to practise in expanded roles and to experience northern life.

What factors are important to keep nurses working in Attawapiskat?

They stay because of the opportunity to practise in an expanded nursing role. The quality of their personal and social life is important, along with job satisfaction.

How do nurses view their role as an RN in Attawapiskat versus an RN in a larger community with physicians and specialists onsite?

Because they practise in expanded roles, their assessment skills are sought and valued by physicians. Expectations are higher from both patients and the health care team.

What strategies do nurses use to deal with cultural differences?

They accept differences, adjust to the local pace of life, and they clarify and validate when unsure about a cultural aspect or practice. They don't judge according to "southern" standards.

Do nurses feel that the community of Attawapiskat receives appropriate health care?

No, they need more visits from physicians and specialists. Consistency in care and equal access to services is a challenge.

What surprises have nurses experienced since moving to Attawapiskat?

They are surprised by their willingness to stay, their ability to meet professional challenges and by their adaptability to the environment and surroundings.

In conclusion, a comment by one nurse that is reflective of many responses given:

"I don't think every nurse could practise up here – personality seems to have something to do with it. Most of us are adventurous, love learning, and seek opportunities and situations to purposely challenge ourselves. You don't have to be here long to feel like you've been here long and to feel like you've known the other nurses for a while. There tends to be a genuine aspect of caring up here – maybe because we realize that for the most part, all we have is each other for support. Generally, no one holds back."

Heather Thomson graduated from the University of Ottawa in 2000 She enjoys her first nursing position in Attawapiskat. Prior to entering nursing, she was a computer programmer for several years.

YOUR AVERAGE NORTHERN NURSE

The Gumboots

You would have to search for aeons, riding time's relentless tide,
To the corners of the Earth, to the globe's far-distant side,
Just to find a job as challenging, as daunting and diverse,
As the never-ending duties of your average northern nurse.

Kate endures the biting cold when it's forty-four below
And tackles blinding storms when polar winds begin to blow.
Liz gets a frantic call in the middle of the night
To a bloody, desperate case that would give ER a fright.

Chorus

> She's an angel of mercy flying through the northern skies
> With a frightened, pregnant woman – *and a baby, oh, surprise!* –
> She's a surgeon when it's needed and she operates alone,
> Guided through the angioplasty by a doctor on the phone.
> She's a steady, patient healer who can manage to be cool
> As she battles flu and scabies at the elementary school.
> She's as sweet as maple syrup, so you'll never hear her curse;
> She's a lot like Super Woman; she's an outpost nurse!

Leanne hopes to get a break and a taste of bigtown life
When she travels to the South – *well, south to Yellowknife!* –
But before she gets her wish, she will have to wait a bit,
'Cause some caribou are grazing on the drifted landing strip.

Then there's Lona, fighting panic, as she flies to hell and back,
'Cause a patient's sinking fast and there's a need for Medivac.
And there's Jan, "Grandma Jan," who counsels, treats, consoles;
Thirty years dispensing love in a hundred different roles.

Repeat Chorus

Lyrics by Bob Macquarrie. Music and Arrangement by Bill Gilday

APPENDIX: COMMUNITY NAMES

Over the years, many names of communities in the North have changed, often more than once. An illustration of such name transitions appeared on the Geographical Names–Aboriginal Communities website of Natural Resources Canada[1].

> As early as 1756 there was a trading post at Great Whale River on the east coast of Hudson Bay. The community was renamed Poste-de-la-Baleine in 1965, and the post office was changed in 1979. The Quebec Commission officially recognized the Inuit name *Kuujjuaraapik* in 1979 for the Inuit part of the village, and *Whapmagoostui* for the Cree part. Canada Post changed the post office to *Kuujjuaraapik* in 1992.

The following information on the place names mentioned in this book has been obtained from this web site and from the Prince of Wales Northern Heritage Centre[2].

Traditional or Former Name	Province / Territory	Official Name	Translation
Aklavik	NWT	Aklarvik	Barren ground grizzly place
Arctic Red River	NWT	Tsiigehtchic	Mouth of the Iron River
Baker Lake	NU	Qamanittuaq	Far inland
Bathurst Inlet	NU	Kinggauk	Like a nose
Bay Chimo (*Uqsuqtuq*)	NU	Umingmaktoc	Place of many muskox
Cambridge Bay	NU	Ikaluktutiak	Good fishing place
Cape Dorset	NU	Kingnait	Mountains
Chesterfield Inlet	NU	Igluligaarjuk	Place with few houses
Clyde River	NU (Baffin)	Kangiqtugaapik	Beautiful cove
Coppermine	NU	Kugluktuk	Place of rapids
Coral Harbour	NU	Sallit	Islands in the south
Edzo	NWT	Edzo	Name of Dene chief
Eskimo Point	NU	Arviat	Bowhead whale
Fort Franklin	NWT	Deline	Moving or flowing water

---

1 http://geonames.nrcan.gc.ca/english/schoolnet/native_names.html
2 Official and Traditional Names for Communities in the NWT and Nunavut, Information Management Group, Indian and Northern Affairs Canada (2000).

Traditional or Former Name	Province / Territory	Official Name	Translation
Fort Good Hope	NWT	Radeyilikoe	Rapids
Fort McPherson	NWT	Teetl'it Zheh	At the head of the waters place
Fort Providence	NWT	Zhahti Kue	Mission house place
Fort Resolution	NWT	Deninue Kue	Moose island place
Fort Smith	NWT	Tthebacha	Beside the rapids
Frobisher Bay	NU (Baffin)	Iqaluit	Place of fish
Garden Creek	AB	Garden River	
Gjoa Haven	NU	Uqsuaqtuuq	Lots of blubber
Great Whale River	QU	Kuujjuaraapik	Great Whale
Hay River	NWT	Xatl'odehchee	Hay river
Holman	NWT	Uluqsaqtuuq	Where there is copper
Inuvik	NWT	Inuuvik	Place of man
Igloolik	NU	Iglulik	Place of houses
Lac La Martre	NWT	Wha Ti	Marten lake
Lansdowne House	ON	Neskantaga	
Norman Wells	NWT	Tlegohti	Where there is oil
Paulatuk	NWT	Paulatuuq	Place of coal
Pelly Bay	NU	Arviliqjuat	Lots of bowhead whales
Pond Inlet	NU (Baffin)	Mittimatalik	Place of Mittima's grave
Port Harrison	QU	Inukjuak	
Rae	NWT	Behchokq	Mbehcho's place
Rankin Inlet	NU	Kangiqtinq	Inlet
Repulse Bay	NU	Naujat	Seagull nesting place
Sachs Harbour	NWT	Ikaahuk	Where you go across to
Saglouc	QU	Salluit	
Snowdrift	NWT	Lutselk'e	Place of the lutsel fish
Spence Bay (Talurruaq)	NU	Taloyoak	Caribou blind
Tuktoyaktuk	NWT	Tukuujaqrtuuq	Looks like a caribou
Whale Cove	NU	Tikirarjuaq	Where many people arrive
Whitedog	ON	Wabassemoong	
Wrigley	NWT	Pedzeh Ki	Clay place
Yellowknife	NWT	Sombak'e	Money place

AFTERWORD

The farthest north that I have been in Canada is Edmonton, so when my friend, Karen, asked me to give her a hand editing a collection of northern nursing stories, I had some misgivings. I realized that my childhood love of reading tales about Arctic and Antarctic explorers, or the hours that Karen and I spent figure skating in an unheated arena did not qualify me for such a task. However, when I started reading the stories she showed me, I couldn't say no.

These are wonderful stories. In many ways, they reflect the oral tradition that is part of the culture of the North. Preparing spoken recollections for publication is not always without challenges. With each story, Karen and I have done our best to preserve the writer's personal style and language.

Working on *Northern Nurses* has been a tremendous learning experience for me. Through these writings, I feel that I have shared in the lives of women and men whom I would be privileged to meet. Their strength of spirit, their selfless dedication to those they serve, and, in the face of all adversities, their unfailing sense of humour – I would love to hear more.

Joan E. Kieser

If you have been associated with the delivery of health care in the Canadian North, and have a story you would like to share, please contact:

jkscottrn@sympatico.ca